Garden Pests
and Predators

The Wildlife in Your Garden
and Its Ecological Control

Elfrida Savigear

Illustrated by Isobel Elsey

BLANDFORD

Blandford
an imprint of Cassell
Villiers House, 41/47 Strand, London WC2N 5JE

Copyright © Elfrida Savigear 1980, 1992

This revised and enlarged edition 1992
First published in 1980 by Thorsons Publishers Limited

British Library Cataloguing in Publication Data
Savigear, Elfrida
  Garden pests and predators. – 2nd. ed.
  1. Gardens. Pests. Control
  I. Title
  635.04996

ISBN 0–7137–2278–9

Distributed in Australia by
Capricorn Link (Australia) Pty Ltd
PO Box 665, Lane Cove, NSW 2066

Typeset by Fakenham Photosetting Ltd, Fakenham, Norfolk
Printed and bound in Great Britain by
Biddles Ltd, Guildford and King's Lynn

CONTENTS

PREFACE   6

1   Garden Residents   7

2   Vertebrates   19

3   Worms   29

4   Snails and Slugs   36

5   Spiders and Mites   39

6   Insects   44

7   Microscopic Organisms   77

8   Control   92

9   Total Activity   104

GLOSSARY   115

SOME COMMON GARDEN PESTICIDES   121

USEFUL ADDRESSES   124

FURTHER READING   125

INDEX   126

PREFACE

Gardens are living places. There is no need to go to a zoo or nature reserve to see a thriving array of wildlife – your garden is filled with millions of organisms. They live in harmony most of the time but, as in any population, there are the misfits. You are also part of this living ecosystem and it is likely that you are the one organism with the greatest influence, because you choose to grow certain plants, remove some vegetation to eat elsewhere and may add manure or fertilizers from another area. This creates an artificial situation. No doubt you have seen gardens which are left to run wild, and have observed that the plants include those weeds you spend many hours removing. So the organisms which depend upon that land for their food and homes will be different too, and if the land is continually left to itself, the organisms will balance out until a stable state results.

But what about your garden? You want it to look attractive, to be highly productive and easy to maintain. How can you encourage beneficial organisms, discourage harmful pests and grow what you like? This book will help you become aware of the living creatures so close at hand, and leads on to show you how you can encourage a healthy garden community.

GARDEN RESIDENTS

No two gardens are the same, but there are two parts to every garden which influence the numerous residents, known and unknown. Gardeners wisely comment on the importance of the soil, but most are unaware of the myriad lifeforms hidden away from observers. Then, of course, the air above the garden is also full of life, and on a warm summer's day many of the creatures will make their presence felt or heard. The two habitats, soil and air, affect the type of organism found, and their life styles are a result of the distinctive environmental properties.

CHARACTERISTICS OF SOIL ORGANISMS

Soil organisms tend to like the dark, stuffy atmosphere. Quite often they will die if exposed to the light or to air, which is drier and richer in oxygen.

Many of the smallest soil organisms (the microscopic ones) move by swimming, and need the soil moisture to get from one place to another. Several soil organisms are anaerobic, which means they are able to respire without oxygen. The soil environment has more gradual temperature changes than the air, especially deeper in the soil, so during the summer months it is a cooler place to live and during the winter it can be the place for avoiding frosts. Mainly for this reason many eggs and larvae develop underground, but it is also possible for these juvenile stages to be sheltered from their enemies by remaining under stones and rotting vegetation. Therefore, many soil organisms are more primitive, with fewer protective features.

CHARACTERISTICS OF AERIAL ORGANISMS

The organisms which live above ground display many more varied features than those confined or living mainly underground. The environmental variations may require special adaptations, as can be seen from Table 1.

Table 1

Environmental Factor	Direct Effect	Result for Organisms
Light	Photosynthesis (food-making by green plants)	Plant growth greatest in the summer, which will encourage an increase in the organisms feeding on plant material
	Dormancy	Plants and animals may be dormant over winter
	Flowering and fruiting	Organisms such as bees and butterflies attracted to the flowers and fruit
Oxygen content	Respiration (converting food into energy)	Aerial organisms can be far more active than soil organisms
Low relative humidity	Most living organisms are at least 80 per cent water	Require some method to control internal water supplies: e.g., hard exoskeleton of beetles
Temperature variations	Extremes can cause death	Require a temperature-control system: e.g., sweat glands in mammals or organisms have the ability to move to cooler, sheltered areas

The obvious differences in the above-ground environment are the diurnal and seasonal light changes, a much lower concentration of carbon dioxide and a higher concentration of oxygen, a low relative humidity (except when it rains!), large temperature variations, air movement ranging to gale-force winds, and a far larger variety of moving organisms to interact with each other. This variety means it is difficult to make generalizations. It is easy to observe that plants are green and use the light to photosynthesize, but can any features of other organisms be linked to aerial environment?

Biological classification is a complicated procedure and it is normal to specialize in one particular facet, such as entomology (the study of insects). But the garden contains organisms from almost every group of living things, so classification and identification may seem a daunting prospect. A gardener needs to be able to place an organism within a general group, and from there identify how it lives and interacts with the rest of the garden.

Large Organisms: Vertebrates

These are probably only visitors to most small gardens, but many town gardens provide homes for rodents, hedgehogs and various birds. The presence of a backbone (vertebrae) and an internal skeleton produces organisms with less protective covering, so they can usually move fast and can carry their food away to a more protected environment. Most of these organisms are well known. They will be considered in the following groups, related to their community activity.

1. Dog, Cat
2. Fox, Badger, Mole, Rabbit
3. Squirrel, Rat, Mouse
4. Hedgehog
5. Toad, Frog
6. Tit, Thrush, Blackbird, Seagull, Starling
7. Pigeon, Bullfinch, Chaffinch, Heron, Sparrow

These macro-organisms are important because their size enables even a single example to have a large influence in a garden, whether due to trampling or earthworks, as in the case of burrowing vertebrates, or due to the voracious appetites which need to be satisfied. Animals in general can be classified as follows:

Carnivorous i.e., feed on animal material
Herbivorous i.e., feed on vegetation
Omnivorous i.e., feed on animal or vegetable material

The carnivores are generally beneficial, whereas the herbivores on a vegetarian diet may cause much damage to important plant material.

Worms, etc.

Ordinary earthworms need no introduction to the gardener, and although there are different species typical of different soil types, they generally influence the garden environment in a similar way. Most gardeners are pleased to see worms, although the exceptionally 'lawn proud' may dislike the casts, and feel worms should be discouraged.

There are various other creatures which come into the worm-type classification. These include the potworms, which are smaller than

9

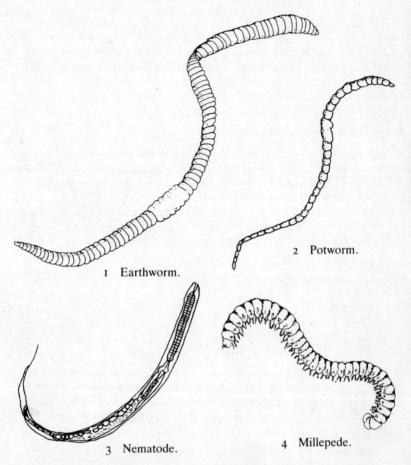

1 Earthworm.

2 Potworm.

3 Nematode.

4 Millepede.

earthworms, are usually grey or white in colour, and are commonly found in compost heaps.

Nematodes (also known as eelworms) are non-segmented worms which are only about 1 mm (1/25 in) in length and are almost colourless, so in normal circumstances they are considered microscopic. Gardeners will come across nematodes, which are pests, but usually the damage provides the only evidence of their presence. There are other nematodes which feed on bacteria and help in the general interaction of communities.

Millepedes and centipedes are long and thin, like worms, and they have segmented bodies. They also have many legs (more than fifteen

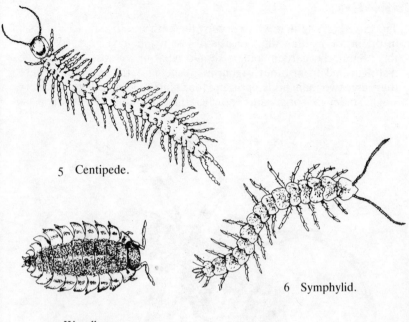

5 Centipede.

6 Symphylid.

7 Woodlouse.

pairs), the millepede with two pairs per segment, the centipede with one pair per segment.

Symphyla are similar to centipedes but they are whitish in colour, quite tiny and have twelve pairs of legs.

Woodlice have been included in this group because they have more legs than the insect group and curl up in a similar fashion to millepedes. They have seven pairs of thoracic legs, with flattened limbs extending from the abdomen.

Insect larvae often appear worm-like and may be found in the sheltered soil environment. They can be distinguished from the worm group because, although they are segmented, they have less than fifteen segments. They will be considered with the insects in Chapter 6.

Slugs, etc.

The mollusc group, or slugs and snails, is probably familiar to most people, although individual species are likely to be less well known. The distinctive characteristics are a muscular foot used for movement along a slime trail, and the presence of a shell. The shell is exterior in the snail and interior in the slug.

Spiders, etc.

The large hairy spiders which occupy the bath are, in fact, a great asset in the house as their diet consists of less hygienic visitors, like blow flies. Similarly, garden spiders should be your friends. They can be distinguished from other organisms, especially the insects, because they have two main body parts and four pairs of jointed legs. The very small, spider-like organisms known as mites include some plant pests.

8   Spider.

Insects

This group of organisms contains many thousands of different species and there is a tremendous amount of variety, making identification a job for the specialist. Many insects have more than one appearance during their development, and some may be pests at one stage and beneficial at another. The most common garden insects have been subdivided into major types which are fairly easily recognized, with a final mixed group containing important extras.

The majority of creepy-crawlies do belong to the insect group, but to be sure of correct classification they should at some stage in their life cycle show the features illustrated in Figure 9.

Aphid Group: e.g., greenfly, blackfly
Aphids can usually be identified by the fact that they reproduce very

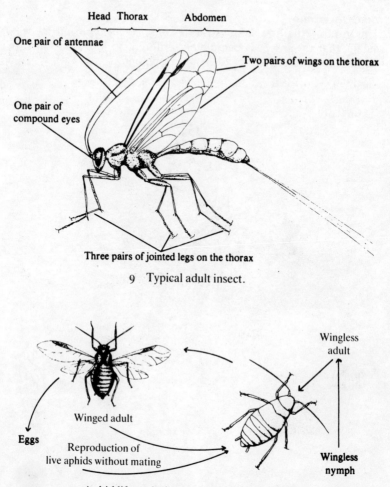

Head Thorax Abdomen

One pair of antennae

Two pairs of wings on the thorax

One pair of
compound eyes

Three pairs of jointed legs on the thorax

9 Typical adult insect.

Wingless
adult

Winged adult

Eggs

Reproduction of
live aphids without mating

Wingless
nymph

10 Aphid life cycle (incomplete metamorphosis).

rapidly to produce colonies which cover soft, fleshy plant material as
they suck out the sugar from the plant. They may often be wingless.

In the nymph stage, the insect looks very similar to the adult
although it is smaller, will never have wings and is unable to reproduce.
This type of life cycle is known as *incomplete metamorphosis*, and it
means identification is easier as the insect has a similar appearance
throughout its life.

There are many other soft-bodied pests in this group, all of which
pierce and suck the plant.

Butterfly Group
This group is the first demonstrating *complete metamorphosis*, which means that the insect is completely different in looks and life style during the different stages of its development.

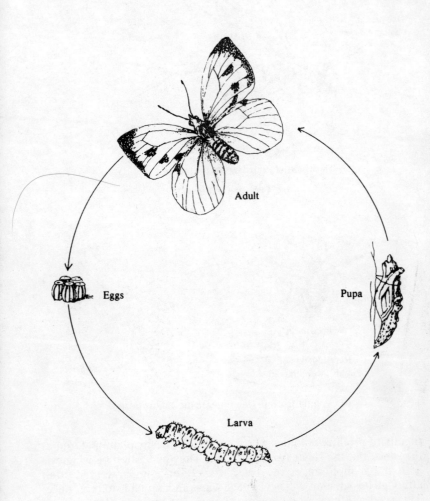

11 Butterfly life cycle (complete metamorphosis).

Fly Group

The true flies have most of the typical insect features (as the adult butterfly) but only one pair of wings and vestigial (withered) hind wings, known as haltares. The larvae, which are frequently pests, are fairly primitive, as they tend to live in a fairly sheltered situation.

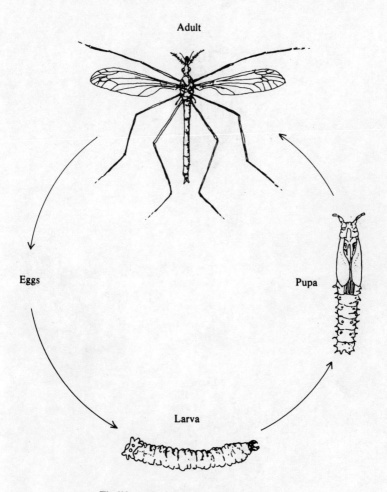

12 Fly life cycle (complete metamorphosis).

Beetle Group
The beetles are the insects in tough armour, as you may have noticed when you have tried to squash one. The armour is produced by a toughening of the front wings to produce elytra, which usually covers the folded hind wings and abdomen. The mouth parts show well-developed mandibles (jaws).

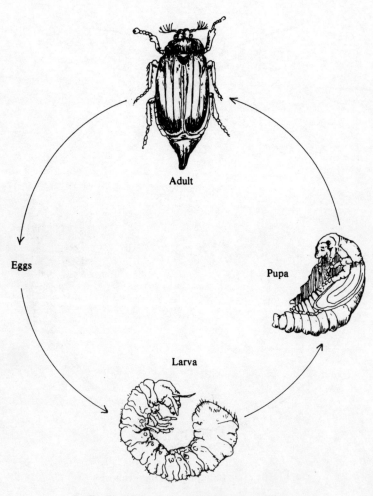

13 Beetle life cycle (complete metamorphosis).

Bee Group
This fairly diverse group covers bees, wasps, sawflies and ants, so it includes both friends and foes of the gardener. The adults show normal insect structure but the two pairs of wings are clear and membranous, and there is a distinct 'waist' between the thorax and abdomen.

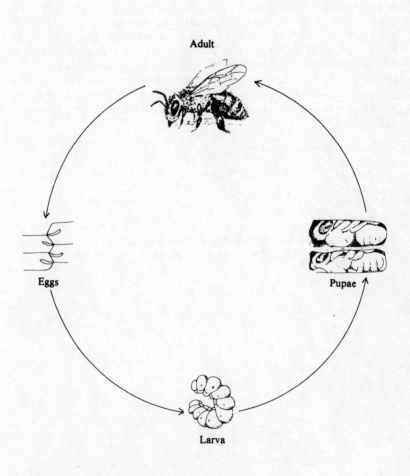

14 Bee life cycle (complete metamorphosis).

Other Insects
Some insects do not fit into any of the previous groups but must be included because they have a distinct influence on the garden environment. Four examples will be described later: the lacewings, dragonflies, earwigs and bush crickets.

Microscopic Organisms

The largest number of organisms in the garden, especially in the soil, will be included in the microscopic section. Evidence of their activity is easily found, such as the tremendous heat produced within a heap of grass cuttings. As they cannot be seen, they can easily be overlooked, but as with all living things, they have their likes and dislikes. It is not normally necessary to identify these micro-organisms down to the tiniest detail, but it is important to understand their life styles so that, wherever possible, the beneficial ones can be encouraged and the harmful ones discouraged. The types of organisms considered more closely in Chapter 7 are:

Microscopic algae
Bacteria
Protozoa
Fungi
Mycorrhiza
Viruses

The fungi may produce macroscopic structures such as toadstools, but the feeding parts, which can be harmful or beneficial, are microscopic.

2

VERTEBRATES

Most of the animals included in this section are visitors rather than permanent residents, although this will depend upon the particular individual and where the garden is situated.

HOUSEHOLD PETS

Household pets which enter the garden can encompass the complete range – I daresay at least one of my readers possesses snakes or an elephant! But the commonest domestic animals in the garden must be dogs and cats. Are they good or bad?

Like many of the other organisms we will mention, they are both beneficial and harmful. They are naturally clean and will make use of the garden for excretory purposes. Bitches tend to use the same area of grass on many occasions, and this will eventually kill the vegetation, because the high concentration of nutrients will prevent the plants taking up water. Dogs tend to go 'little and often', which usually produces less conspicuous results, unless they happen to be marking territory such as a gateway hedge. Tom cats are very similar to dogs in their behaviour, but cats in general try to bury their excrement and any freshly dug soil (especially where seeds have been planted!) is a great attraction. They usually seem to use every garden except their own, which is rather unfortunate for the non-cat-lover. Cats also like to catch birds and sometimes they will steal fledgelings and prevent them growing to adulthood.

The main benefit of these animals is no doubt their companionship, but they also serve a useful function in warding off pests. Some birds delight in eating freshly planted seeds or young seedlings; others are partial to fresh raspberries and plums. Here the dog or cat will probably need no encouragement to chase them off. Both animals are useful in catching rodents such as rats or mice, although we humans are not always too pleased when the catch is presented inside the house!

BURROWING VERTEBRATES

The next few vertebrate animals are considered together because their main influence upon the garden is similar, due to their burrowing activities. Most of them are found mainly in the larger gardens and more rural areas, but foxes especially are becoming much more common in town gardens. From the gardener's point of view, they must all be classed as pests, but some naturalists would be quite pleased to have a close 'viewing' site.

Foxes

Foxes live in earths, which are semi-underground dens, preferably in sandy soil, but they will also take over other animals' homes, such as large rabbit holes. Cubs are usually born in spring. The dog will remain with the vixen during her pregnancy and for a while after the birth. Foxes feed on rats, mice, rabbits, birds, frogs, earthworms and beetles, but more recently they have become scavengers at dustbins and refuse tips. They have always been known to take the occasional lamb.

Badgers

Badgers are really only visitors in rural areas and, as they are very shy creatures, few people see them. They live in sets, which are underground homes in well-drained soil, usually in a wooded situation. They feed during the night on a mixed diet including rabbits, earthworms, slugs and snails, fruit, nuts and grass. They are useful predators, and in most garden situations they need not be destroyed.

Moles

Moles are also shy creatures, but their presence is soon announced by molehills, the small mounds of earth produced while they dig their underground tunnels. They have specialized 'spade' forelimbs, which easily move the soil out of the way. While digging, the mole will disturb earthworms, insects, millepedes and slugs and snails, and these make up its diet.

Rabbits

Rabbits are the last main burrowing garden visitors, and once more they are confined to rural or semi-rural areas. Their warrens can be large, especially in a sandy bank, but they are unlikely to burrow in the more formal type of garden. They are herbivorous and so may be a nuisance, grazing new shoots and even removing the bark from young trees.

RODENTS

The rodents are a large group of mammals. Most of them are shy but they may leave a visiting card of some sort.

Grey Squirrels

Grey squirrels are very common visitors to gardens if there are any large deciduous trees around in which they can make their nest or drey. They are especially fond of acorns, but their diet is wide-ranging and includes other types of nut, cones and other fruits, bulbs, grain, plant material and bark, fungi and various insects.

Rats

Rats always present a picture of unpleasant events, such as plagues, and the criticisms have some justification. Few gardens will be visited by rats unless there are neglected buildings to provide shelter. Rats traditionally feed on grain, but their diet includes insects, mice and plant material, and they also scavenge around waste places.

Mice

Mice are much more common visitors, and although they create fear in many humans, they are really fairly harmless.

Wood mice live in a tunnel system among rotting vegetation, so they are sometimes disturbed in the compost heap. They are active during the dark hours, when they search out seeds, their favourite food. At other seasons of the year they may feed on insect larvae.

House mice, as the name suggests, like a more sheltered existence, but they can sometimes be found in garden sheds. They are omnivorous, enjoying plant material, insects and flesh from larger mammals too.

Voles

Some years voles can also be quite common in the garden, making their nests in long vegetation or among straw or other mulches at the base of plants. This gives the timid creatures shelter. They will gnaw away at the base of trees and shrubs, and if this continues all the way round, the growing tissue or cambium will be damaged and the plant will die. Voles are able to feed on tough plant material because they are equipped with both the normal chisel-like biting teeth and also a very efficient set of grinders. Some species are more fond of other plant material, such as berries, buds and bulbs, but fortunately they are themselves prey to the household cat!

HEDGEHOGS

Hedgehogs are very distinctive creatures and most people have a soft spot for them. Many of them become quite tame, and call regularly for a supper of bread and milk. Gardeners are wise to encourage hedgehogs as they feed on many of our problem pests. However, it should perhaps be pointed out that they harbour many fleas, and dogs and cats

15 Hedgehog – a friend to be encouraged.

will pick these up, although this flea species is not so fond of the domestic host. Their hair has become modified into sharp spines which protect them from predators – except the motor car. If a hedgehog falls on to its back, the spines will not hurt it as each one is embedded in a thick layer of muscular material. They nest in sheltered shrubbery both when they are caring for their young, mainly during the summer, and when they hibernate during the winter months. Their diet is varied but they are particularly partial to slugs, earthworms, insects, mice, frogs, berries and other plant material. They are noisy foragers so they may often be heard grunting and snorting in the undergrowth.

TOADS AND FROGS

Toads

Toads and frogs are easily recognized but quite often people find it hard to distinguish between the two. Toads are more solidly built than frogs, with shorter hind legs and a dull, dry, pimply skin which enables

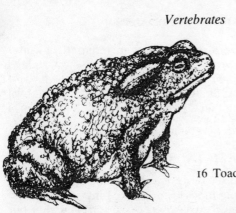

16 Toad – with a voracious appetite.

them to merge into the background. They will rest camouflaged for many hours, and this enables them to survive the attacks of many would-be predators. They jump using all four feet and this makes them appear rather clumsy. They produce an offensive fluid when attacked by birds, and this leaves them safer from enemy attack. Toads feed on many different fauna, including beetles, caterpillars, snails, worms, woodlice and mice, and seem to have an insatiable appetite. They establish a definite 'home' under a stone or sheltered by a root, and although they may travel some distance to feed, they usually return to this home. They need a pond for their gelatinous string of spawn, but the remainder of their life is on land and is mainly determined by the abundance of insect life as a food source.

Frogs

Frogs have smoother, yellowish-green skins and long hind legs adapted for jumping. Once more water is essential for breeding and

17 Frog – hungry for slugs, worms and insects.

tadpole development, and damp, muddy places are required for winter hibernation. But frogs are voracious feeders on slugs, worms and insects, and they can jump their way some distance from the nearest pond. Obviously you are most likely to see frogs if you have your own pond, but frogs from a neighbour's pond will be quite likely to visit your garden and should certainly be encouraged.

BENEFICIAL BIRDS

Most people are delighted to see birds in a garden and British people spend a lot of money on various foods to encourage bird visitors. Many birds are beneficial too, as they feed on insect pests, and even when our feathered friends eat all our soft fruit they seem to be forgiven in a way that slugs or caterpillars never are.

Blackbirds are one of the commonest garden birds and they are especially welcome because of their tuneful songs. They are very partial to earthworms, but although this could possibly be beneficial if

18 Blackbird – a helpful songster.

they remove them from lawns, it is mainly detrimental to soil structure. They also eat many larvae and adult insects and so they are more welcome than not.

Starlings are not such popular visitors as they tend to be noisy and untidy and often frighten off smaller, more attractive birds. They are very fond of brightly coloured berries, but it is possible to protect plants by nets; their other diet includes insects, especially leatherjackets.

19 Starling – noisy, but devours many insect larvae.

20 Thrush – fond of snails.

Thrushes are also welcome visitors, especially if your garden is troubled by snails, and quite commonly a tapping sound in the garden will be a thrush banging a snail against a stone, and later having a juicy morsel for its reward. Thrushes do not restrict their diet to snails, also eating other insects and small animals, and they enjoy fruit as a sweetmeat.

Robins seem a very 'British' institution, and because they have distinct territories, they may become quite tame. They like any soft, juicy morsel – which means they will not stop to decide whether their prey is beneficial or harmful! However, as one of their favourite foods is the caterpillar, we can perhaps forgive them for eating the occasional worm.

Tits are delightful birds, partly because of their colourful attire but also because they are somewhat cheeky. Their diet is almost entirely confined to insects, so they are high on the list of beneficial birds. If the winter is hard, most insects or larvae will be destroyed or well hidden, so tits will be grateful for a supply of nuts and also a bowl of unfrozen water! Do not worry if tits appear to be pecking at unopened buds – they are gently looking for insects and insect eggs and they rarely cause any harm.

Seagulls are also garden visitors, and they use their beaks to hook out insects and larvae which are sheltering beneath the soil.

FEATHERED PESTS

Unfortunately, some birds must really be classed as garden pests because they do such a lot of damage. Top of the list may be the bullfinch, a most colourful bird but one whose beauty is but a mask for devilry! As they have fairly soft beaks, they need to feed on softer material, and so they are often to be found enjoying soft fruit. However, they are more likely to be seen attacking the blossoms and buds of many trees and shrubs. Sometimes they work so quickly, pecking out the buds of cherry trees, that it is hard to believe they have time to enjoy anything.

21 Bullfinch – a colourful devil.

Chaffinches may also damage flower buds, but this is usually less common.

Sparrows are often a nuisance in springtime, when they are particularly attracted to crocuses. This is for a good reason, as the flowers contain a supply of vitamin A, but it is annoying to have one of our earliest spring flowers pulled to pieces.

Pigeons seem always to make their presence known by their powerful coos, a sound which may seem pleasant at first but can become very irritating after a while. They can be a dreadful nuisance, searching out newly planted seeds and also feeding on seeds such as peas and beans. During the winter months they will peck away at winter greens, and, of course, they frighten off smaller birds and can empty a bird table very rapidly!

22 Pigeon – hungry for seeds.

Herons are beautiful birds and I am always thrilled to watch one flying over, but they are becoming common garden pests as thieves, stealing goldfish from ponds.

23 Heron – a visitor looking for goldfish.

WORMS

This chapter tells of the activities of garden organisms which are fairly small, are long and thin in shape and tend to wriggle or crawl around the ground. The most common of these is probably the earthworm, which has a very interesting life history.

EARTHWORMS

Earthworms have been observed by many naturalists and Darwin wrote a book about worm activity on plant material. Scientists are still busy investigating worm action, and the more the work proceeds, the more important and intriguing worms prove to be.

There are just over twenty species of earthworm found in Britain. Worms characteristically have up to 150 cylindrical segments, and four pairs of bristles on the lower half of almost every segment (see Fig. 1 on page 10). They are pinkish brown in colour and usually have a distinct band or clitellum about one third of the way from the head end. The skin possesses glands which produce mucus over the surface of the worm to prevent desiccation and to facilitate movement through the soil. There are light-receptive cells in the worm's skin, and these warn it to burrow down to safety again when you bring it to the surface by your digging. There is a simple brain at the mouth end of the worm and a main nerve which passes all the way down its body.

Reproduction

Earthworms are hermaphrodite, possessing both male and female sex organs in different parts of their bodies. But they still have to mate to exchange their sperm with another worm. The commonest earthworm mates above ground, but the majority of species hide away underground. Two worms become bound together with mucus, the sperm are exchanged and later the worms separate. The clitellum produces a skin-like secretion which gradually hardens and the worm then wriggles backwards out of this tube, which closes to become the cocoon.

The eggs are in the cocoon first, and the sperm are picked up as the cocoon moves over the worm's body. The eggs are fertilized externally, and the young worm develops to emerge between one and five months later. Young worms tend to be colourless on hatching but usually show all their segments. They continue to grow at rates varying with temperature and moisture and will be sexually mature in one to two years. They may live for about six years, but this is very dependent upon predators, disease and chemicals.

Regeneration

It is a commonly held view that if you cut a worm in half, two worms will be produced. Regeneration can occur, but you are more likely to kill the worm. Regeneration occurs most readily when a worm loses a few of the segments at its posterior end, but it will not take place if too much of the tissue is damaged. New growth is also most efficient in warm temperatures and when worms are young.

The Gardener's Friend

Earthworms are beneficial organisms to the normal soil because they burrow through, thus increasing the aeration and drainage. They also feed on and break down organic material such as leaves. They burrow through the soil by alternately contracting and relaxing the longitudinal and circular muscles in the body wall. As they move, in fact, they eat the soil in front of them. This is mixed with moisture and other waste food material and excreted as the cast. Within the burrow, the cast is pressed against the burrow walls, and some fungi will grow on this, releasing nutrients and breaking down the organic matter even further. The shape and depth of the burrow depends on the species of earthworm, but most of them are active in the first 300 mm (12 in) of the soil. If the weather is very cold or very dry, they will burrow deeper to find a more amenable clime. They feed on plant and fungal material and the preference seems to be for soft, deciduous leaves if they are available, though some species are fond of animal dung. All worms need calcium carbonate as they secrete this with their digestive juices, and this is probably the reason why they are normally absent from acid soils and do not like eating leaves from coniferous trees.

You can encourage earthworms in various ways. They are most active in fairly well-drained, alkaline, loamy soils, where there is plenty of organic matter for them to feed upon. They will like your activities in the vegetable plot and their burrows will bring air to the roots, encouraging good growth. They continue to mix the soil up and bring nutrient-rich soil to the surface. They are very active beneath grass and here they help to produce a stone-free, crumb soil. It is unfortunate that worm-casts on lawns prompt some gardeners to kill worms, because their lawn will become less well drained and they will have to spike it instead of allowing the worms to do the work for them. One fairly effective way to discourage worms from the surface is to treat your lawn with ammonium sulphate fertilizer. This supplies nitrogen, which will encourage green, healthy growth, but it also makes the soil more acid and this will make the worms stay below ground.

POTWORMS

Potworms (see Fig. 2 on page 10) are most commonly seen as active components of the compost heap. They are small, grey or whitish worms which wriggle actively when they are disturbed. They tend to be found in groups around good food sources, and they seem to enjoy rotting plant material, fungi, bacteria and eelworms. They are thought to control some eelworm pests by feeding on young stages.

NEMATODES

Nematodes or roundworms (see Fig. 3 on page 10) are found in an amazing variety of habitats. The majority of them continue life without our noticing them. It is within this group that many 'worm' parasites are found, partly because they feed by absorbing liquid food, in this case from their host. Others are found in the garden, mainly as harmless soil organisms, but sometimes feeding on plants and causing damage. Most of these nematodes are very tiny and almost colourless, so they certainly do not draw attention to their presence.

The Nematode Life Cycle

The life cycle is fairly simple and straightforward. Male and female worms mate and eggs are laid, protected by a tough protein wall. The eggs hatch to produce tiny worms, which are protected by a tough cuticle. As the juvenile worm grows, it has to moult because the cuticle is too tough to expand. It moults four times before it is adult.

Nematodes move by an eel-like swimming motion, brought about by contraction and relaxation of the muscular body against the tough, protective cuticle.

Feeding Habits

The nematodes which live freely in the soil (and some estimations have found more than 10 million per square metre/11 square feet of soil) feed mainly in the top 50 mm (2 in). They feed on algae, protozoa and bacteria, rotting organic matter and also other nematodes. They do not have any obvious effect upon the soil, but as they feed on other organisms they must be important in maintaining a balanced society.

Parasitic Nematodes (Eelworms)

There are several different types of nematodes which are considered pests, but the ones which are probably most widespread are known as migratory root eelworms. These parasitize plant roots at some stage during their lives, but they can also swim from plant to plant and in this way they are possibly the second-largest offenders for virus transmission (aphids top the list). They differ from normal soil nematodes by having a hollow spear inside their mouths and this they use to pierce plant cells before they inject their digestive juices and suck out the sap. Nematodes or eelworms feeding on roots are very difficult to spot and frequently other organisms, such as fungi or bacteria, enter when the nematode has damaged the plant tissue. This continues to make the plant stunted and look sick, but if the plant is pulled up the rotted roots fall off and the eelworms remain in the soil to swim off to some new site of attack. The best way of control is obviously to avoid the pest, but soil sterilants do give fairly effective control. Alternatively it is possible to grow plants of the *Tagetes* genus (marigolds) and plough these into the soil before a susceptible crop is planted. This will reduce the population of eelworms.

Cyst Eelworms

These eelworms are especially troublesome pests because they are so difficult to control. They enter the root at the second larval stage and swim between the cells until they reach the centre of the root, where the cells are rich in nutrients. The eelworms produce saliva, which makes the plant cells greatly enlarge and results in a weak and stunted plant.

Leaf Eelworms

Leaf eelworms feed on leaf tissue by entering through the leaf stomatal pores. They swim from one area to another by making use of dew, rain or water from the can or hose. One of the commonest is chrysanthemum eelworm, and the first visible signs are when yellow discolorations appear between the veins of the lower leaves. Later the leaves will turn black and flop down against the stem. Any eelworms within the dead tissue dry up and become curled like a watchspring. In this condition they can remain dormant for several months. When moisture is available they then continue as before.

24 Eelworm damage to fern fronds.

Stem Eelworms
Stem eelworms enter the plant through small wounds or through plant pores such as lenticels. Once within the plant they feed on the plant tissues, causing swellings and commonly rotting.

MILLEPEDES

Millepedes (see Fig. 4 on page 10) are related to insects as they have jointed legs, but they have many more legs, though the 'thousand' of their name is rather an exaggeration. Their bodies are constructed of between twenty and sixty segments, most of which have two pairs of legs.

There are two main groups of harmful millepedes, commonly referred to as the snake millepede and the flat millepede. The snake millepedes have hard, cylindrical bodies and live in the soil, feeding on organic matter and plant roots, especially where the roots have already been weakened by some other organism, or on soft material such as seedlings or germinating seeds. The flat millepedes are shorter, with flatter bodies and longer legs (these are the ones which are often found in the greenhouse). Pill millepedes are also common – their name a reference to the fact they roll into a ball when they are disturbed.

Millepedes tend to be far less active than centipedes, so if you see a many-legged, worm-like creature disappearing from view, it was most likely to have been a centipede. Millepedes have poorly developed mouthparts, which means they are unable to feed on any tough material, but are much more fond of fungi and rotting organic matter, so they will be found in greatest numbers in a soil rich in organic matter or near the compost heap. Some of them are unable to digest the cellulose of plant cell walls, so they have to devour large quantities of organic material to obtain sufficient food for energy. This means they begin to break down organic material, which can then be attacked by other soil micro-organisms. Millepedes are protected by a cuticle which they produce using calcium, so they like soil with free calcium. They will suffer from desiccation, though, and this is why in drought conditions some of them are tempted to suck the moisture from plant roots.

CENTIPEDES

Centipedes (see Fig. 5 on page 11) can be distinguished from millepedes because they possess only one pair of legs per body segment, and the number of segments varies between species from as few as fifteen to over 100. They have a tough outer coat but do not possess the waterproofing cuticle present in millepedes. They can move very efficiently with their many legs; if you look at them closely, you will see that they have made life easier by having each leg slightly longer than the one on the previous segment. Centipedes tend to be predacious, so their mouths are equipped with powerful jaws for biting and with poison claws, which they use to immobilize their prey before eating. They feed on protozoa, mites, insects, slugs and worms, and they are also cannibalistic, especially if the other centipede is wounded.

Centipede eggs are usually soft and are laid in the soil, so they are not easy to find. The young centipedes develop by a series of moults. In some species they look very similar to the adult, apart from the fact that their legs are shorter, but the young centipedes, which live under stones, begin life with only seven pairs of legs and it takes four moults before they have developed the normal fifteen pairs.

SYMPHYLA

Symphyla (see Fig. 6 on page 11) are organisms very similar to millepedes and centipedes, because they have an elongated body composed of fifteen segments and twelve pairs of legs. The common species found in greenhouses and gardens in Britain is whitish in colour and only about 8 mm (⅓ in) long. They are very active creatures, and tend to burrow deeper into the soil as soon as they are disturbed. They feed on dead and dying plant material, but also enjoy any plants with succulent root systems, completely destroying root hairs and small roots. These wounds often provide entry for bacteria and fungi, so plant deaths may easily be attributed to the wrong cause. Correct diagnosis of symphylid damage is best achieved by soaking the soil and plant in a bucket of water, as the symphyla will then float to the surface among the other debris.

WOODLICE

Woodlice (see Fig. 7 on page 11) are fairly distinctive creatures and cannot really be described as long and thin, but as they can be confused with pill millepedes, they have been included in this group. The remainder of the organisms which belong to the same class, the Crustacea, are water organisms, which is why woodlice like moist situations.

They have oval-shaped bodies, the back of which is protected by tough plates, and their lower surfaces show seven pairs of walking legs and two pairs of antennae, although one pair is very small. One common species is known as the pill-bug, as it rolls into a ball when it is disturbed.

The female woodlouse lays her eggs in early summer and carries them around in a pouch underneath her body. When the young hatch, they continue to be carried around by the female until the first moult. They are white when young, and have only six pairs of legs.

Woodlice feed mainly on rotting plant material but they also like rotting animal material. They live in environments where they can retain moisture, so you find them under rockery stones, under cloches or in the greenhouse. If you are a tidy gardener, there is probably not much rotting material around, so they may be tempted to nibble at roots and stems at ground level, and at seedlings.

4

SNAILS AND SLUGS

Snails and slugs are distinctive animals, mainly because of the way they move on their thick, muscular foot along a mucus or slime trail. Few gardeners have a kind word for these creatures, as it is hard to find any good aspects (except the praise they seem to be giving you when they eat well off your vegetables!). My soil is heavy clay, so I see many of these creatures. Although I find them hard to love, I will try to tell you enough so that you can at least take an interest in their life history.

SNAILS

Snails are often really attractive creatures because their shells can show many distinctive, intricate patterns. The shell is made of a tough outer layer and an inner layer of calcium carbonate, and this explains why snails are more predominant on alkaline soils. If you lift up a snail to examine it, the head and body will rapidly be withdrawn into the shell and it will produce a mass of froth, which is unattractive to many would-be predators. If you put the snail down again and wait patiently,

25 Garden snail – with head extended showing the two pairs of tentacles.

it will soon try to see if the danger has passed and will push out its head. The head has two pairs of tentacles, the eyes being found at the ends of the longer pair.

The eyes are not very good, allowing visibility only up to 100 mm (4 in), but they are light-responsive. As a result the snail prefers shade during the day and dull light at night. The same tentacles respond to smell and taste, and some snails have been shown to sense lettuces from a distance of 600 mm (2 ft) or so. Their bodies have a tough, leathery skin which is made up of a coiled hump and a muscular foot. There is a type of lung within the shell, and you can see it open and close if you watch the area between the head and the shell.

Feeding

The mouth is made of two jaws, the lower of which has a long, rasping tongue known as the radula. This is composed of bands of hooked teeth, about 150 of them along the length of the tongue by just over 100 across. These teeth gradually wear away from the front end, but will be replaced from special tissues deeper inside the mouth. The radula is very effective at rubbing off the outer tissue of leaves, so the snail can then feed on the inner tissue. Often bacteria and fungi cause the plant material to rot and many snails would rather eat dead or dying material if it is available. However, they will certainly attack living plants and graze off seedlings.

Mating

Snails usually hibernate from late October onwards, not emerging again until spring. During late spring they mate, usually at night. There is an elaborate courtship ceremony during which the pair remain in contact by their muscular feet. After a while they send a 'love dart' – a hard, ridged, pointed dart which shoots into the skin of the partner snail. This is followed by exchange of sperm between the hermaphrodite pair. The eggs are small, white and gelatinous. Laid in the soil in collections of about fifty, they are covered over and left. About twenty-five days later small snails will emerge.

SLUGS

Slugs are pests in most gardens except the very dry, and even then the British climate usually provides a damp season at some time during the winter months. They may have beautiful colours and decoration, but few people spend long looking at them closely. They are very similar to snails but have no shells to escape into. A few forms retain a tiny external shell at the hind ends of their bodies, but in the majority the shell is reduced to a stronger area within the muscular body.

26 Slug – showing the tough, muscular body.

Feeding

They feed with a radula on leaves, stems, bulbs, tubers, fungi, algae and animal material. They have been found to feed on aphids and small flies, so they do have a beneficial aspect. They require a moist environment, so you will find them hiding under leaves or stones during the daytime. If you remove dying vegetation, you will remove not only some of their daytime hideouts but also some of their food sources, and they may then be encouraged to visit the more healthy plant material, so beware. Their eggs are similar to snails' eggs and will be found in groups in moist soil or among rotting vegetation as these habitats provide protection from frost and drought. During warm weather the eggs will hatch in a few weeks, but during the winter they may remain dormant until the following spring. Young slugs look like miniature versions of the adult, and their growth rate is very greatly influenced by the environment. The garden slug is not mature for two years, but field slugs may mature in five months.

5

SPIDERS AND MITES

Mites and spiders are distinguished from the insects because they have four pairs of legs. Mites are very tiny and have only one body section, whereas the spiders have two body parts, a fused head and thorax, and the abdomen beyond a waist-like region. I will concentrate on the spiders first of all, and then progress to the smaller but no less significant mites.

SPIDERS

Spiders have figured prominently in folklore and tradition and although many people find them rather worrying, few would kill them intentionally. This is a good thing as they are carnivorous and feed on all stages of many of our insect pests.

Spiders (see Fig. 8 on page 12) are not equipped with antennae but have a pair of palps at the front of their head, and these are used as sense organs for smelling and feeling. Male spiders have clubbed palps, which have an additional function, for inserting sperm into the female's body. The jaws are pincer-like and include a poison gland which is used to immobilize the prey. Just above the jaws are eight simple eyes. Two are used for 'long-distance' viewing, two give a wide field of view and the others help the spider to stalk and catch its prey.

Not all spiders produce webs but they will produce silk for other purposes, such as making the protective cocoon around their eggs. The abdomen contains special silk glands, and the silk squeezes out through tiny pores in the spinnarets, which are found at the tip of the abdomen. When a web or cocoon is being produced, the spider often guides the silk into the correct formation by using its back legs.

Web Spiders

Web spiders are perhaps the most obvious, especially on damp mornings when their webs have a silvery glow, as each drop of water acts as a minute lens reflecting the light. These webs are to catch food, and at dusk you will often see the spider sitting in the centre, waiting. If an insect becomes trapped in the web, it will struggle, and the movement on the fine silk strands warns the spider, who will immediately trace the signal and find the prisoner. The spider bites the insect, injecting some poison to subdue its activity, and then she will wrap the captive up in a silk trap. She may eat the food immediately or wait until some time later. You may wonder why I have referred to the spider as 'she'. This is quite simply because the adult male spider spends his rather hazardous life courting rather than eating! He also has to approach the female spider via the web, and she frequently attacks him, so persever-ance is essential. Male garden spiders usually manage to mate several times during the summer, but by the autumn their energy is used up and they are often eaten by their last mistress.

Wolf Spiders

Wolf spiders are also common garden inhabitants, and they are mainly found scuttling in and out of low-growing plants. They are called wolf spiders because their front pair of legs is longer than the other three pairs, and they use these legs to catch prey after a hunt. They like to rest in the sunshine, but they will always be on the lookout for any tasty morsel passing by, and then they will stir into action. Wolf spiders care for their young in a more active way than the spiders that produce webs. Once the female has laid her eggs and bound them into a silken cocoon, she picks the cocoon up with her jaws and carries it around, suspended beneath her abdomen but held in place by a few extra strands of silk. The cocoon is often a very bulky addition to her body, but she will still wander in and out and over vegetation at great speed. When the eggs are ready to hatch, in early July or so, the mother spider weaves a tent-shaped web and sits on guard outside. The spiderlings remain in the tent until moulting, and even then they may ride around on the mother's back.

HARVESTMEN

Harvestmen belong to the same group as spiders but their bodies are all in one piece and they tend to have extremely long legs, with the second pair the longest. These legs are very important sense organs, used for detecting the scent of valuable food materials. They have only two eyes, which project above the head end of the body. They are carnivorous animals, being very partial to a wide range of the smaller fauna. Many of them also enjoy fungi and rotting vegetation, especial-ly as a source of moisture.

MITES

Mites are tiny animals often only just visible to the human eye, but if they are examined with a lens they are found to have a rounded body and four pairs of legs. Many of the mites feed on living plant material

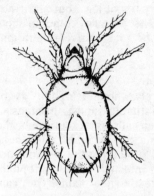

27 Mite – a tiny organism with four pairs of legs.

and have mouthparts adapted for piercing plants and sucking out the sap. Only a few are really serious pests, but there are also several important predatory mites and others which live in the soil, breaking down organic matter and fungi.

Red Spider Mites

Red spider mites are very tiny, with bodies between 0.3 and 0.7 mm (less than $\frac{1}{50}$ in) in length, so they are seen only as minuscule reddish dots moving around on the lower surface of leaves. There are various different species, such as the bryobia mites, the fruit tree red spider mite and the very common glasshouse red spider mite, which is more correctly called the two-spotted spider mite.

When looked at closely the two-spotted spider mite is found to be yellow and to have two fairly large black spots on either side of its body. All three mites attack quite a wide range of plants, but the damage is relatively similar. The leaves show a fine yellow speckling, which may extend until the whole leaf is yellow or bronzed and becomes rather brittle or papery, due to dehydration of the tissues. Mites can also transmit viral diseases if they feed first on an infected plant and later on a healthy one. The glasshouse red spider mite produces a silk webbing which can stunt plant growth and cause distortion. In a warm environment, it will reproduce all year round, though the rate of reproduction slows quite rapidly at cooler temperatures. In an unheated glasshouse it will hibernate in the glasshouse structure and reappear the following year. The outdoor species survives the winter as bright-red eggs, laid in cracks or crevices in bark to protect them from the winter frosts. When the young hatch, the larval form has only three pairs of legs, but after the first moult it will be found to have four pairs. Maturity comes in about one month, so most summers there will be four or five generations, allowing for large numbers to develop.

Gall Mites

Galls are mentioned elsewhere in this book as abnormal plant growths due to some external stimulus, and many mites have this effect. One of the commonest garden galls is blackcurrant big bud, which is produced when the gall mites suck inside buds and stimulate the bud tissue and contents to swell up. Sometimes the bud may open to show abnormal leaves and flowers. If infected buds are left on the bush, the mites will develop fully and spread to new plants. They can act as vectors for the

28 Mite damage produces blackcurrant big bud.

virus disease known as 'reversion'. Heavy pruning at an early stage will often prevent severe damage from big bud, but if virus infection ensues, the plants must be dug up and burnt.

Other gall mites may also be found but most can be treated merely as interesting garden residents, as harmful effects are virtually negligible.

For example, you may find blister galls on walnut leaves, or bright-red nail or pimple galls on sycamores and related members of the genus *Acer*.

Galls make quite a fascinating study (see British Plant Gall Society, page 124).

Predatory Mites

Usually predators feed on entirely different types of organism from their own, but in the mites there are examples of cannibalism. On fruit trees, for example, where there are mite pests, there can be up to nine species of predatory mites. They seem to hibernate as adult females, so only about 10 per cent survive a normal winter. In April–May they lay individual, colourless, ovoid eggs on the lower surfaces of the newly expanding leaves. The eggs hatch to a larva with three pairs of legs, but after the first moult the nymphs have four pairs of legs. The nymphs and adults are predacious on spider mites and gall mites and their eggs. If there are no tasty mites available, these predatory mites can survive by feeding on leaves, but they need animal protein if they are to reproduce.

Two-spotted spider mites have been successfully controlled in many cases by using the predator *Phytoseiulus persimilis*. The mites are a yellowish-orange colour with pear-shaped bodies, and they develop at twice the rate of the pest. The female predators are very efficient at searching out adult spider mites, and the young feed on the immature pests. The predator cannot live without its prey, so if it does the job very efficiently, it will eventually kill itself off, at which point new supplies of predator have to be introduced. As these are both mites, chemical control of the pest should normally be avoided. If you have not introduced enough predators to give efficient control of the pest, an acaricide may be sprayed on the young tips of the plants as it is here that newly emerged pests congregate while the predator is concentrating on eating their relatives.

6

INSECTS

The largest number of all organisms is found in the group known as the insects. Obviously there are many very different-looking types of insects, but they have certain basic characteristics which unite them in the one group. They all belong to the phylum *Arthropoda*, which describes the jointed legs and hard outer skeleton. The insect order is the largest one, but there are three other orders in the *Arthropoda*: the *Arachnida*, which is the group containing the mites and spiders (see Chapter 5); the *Crustacea*, in which the woodlouse is included (see Chapter 3); and the *Myriapoda*, which contains the millepedes and centipedes (see Chapter 3).

In Chapter 1 I divided the common insects into different groups with a very brief description to help with identification. Only the adults show important insect characteristics (see Fig. 9 on page 13) and the many different larval forms may prove rather confusing. In fact you should find after a while that the larval forms also fit into general groups, and I suggest that you look carefully at the life-cycle diagrams to notice the general features in each case.

APHIDS

Most gardeners are only too well aware of aphids and it is unlikely that they are popular with anyone. They are obviously very successful as a group and they have been studied in detail to try to find some way of reducing their activities as pests.

Reproduction

Let us begin with their life history. They are far less complicated than many insects and undergo incomplete metamorphosis. This means that the aphid egg hatches into a nymph, or a small aphid similar to the adult except it has no wings and is unable to reproduce. That is the traditional way the aphid reproduces, but it is extra successful in that the female can also reproduce without mating (see Fig. 10 on page 13).

This is why an aphid colony grows so rapidly, as reproduction is directly related to good conditions. Imagine an aphid having found your crop of broad beans – what an ideal place to bring up a colony!

If you look closely at a colony of aphids you will also see that many of the insects are wingless. This is another adaptation to an ideal environment. These aphids may well be mature and able to reproduce, but as there is already a good supply of food, there is no need to move on to find another one. When the conditions start to get overcrowded in a colony, the new aphids will develop wings and fly off to find a fresh source of food and start a new colony.

Feeding Habits

Aphids are specially equipped with mouthparts to enable them to suck the sugar out of plants. They pierce through the plant cell walls with their stylet, and as the plant sap is under pressure they are able to absorb food without much effort. They tend to enjoy softer, more succulent plant material, and leave the tougher, more woody plants to

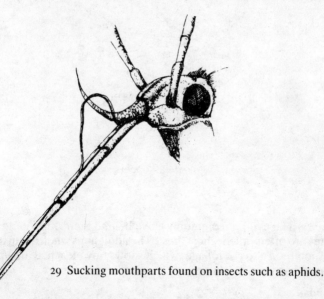

29 Sucking mouthparts found on insects such as aphids.

others. The aphids exude 'honeydew' from the anus: this is excess sugar from the plant sap which is produced because they have to feed on such a lot of sap to get sufficient protein. The honeydew covers the leaves with a sticky layer and is often a food source for the black fungus sooty mould, which disfigures the leaves and reduces the light reaching the plant for food-making.

There are a lot of other important insects in a similar group to the aphids because their method of feeding is by sucking.

Froghoppers

These are the small insects which produce cuckoo spit, the froth you see on plant stems. The nymphs live in the froth to avoid drying out and it protects them from would-be predators. The adults leap and this action is thought to look frog-like, hence their name.

Leafhoppers

These are small insects found mainly on leaves. They are relatively host-specific, which means each species feeds only on a small range of plants, but like the aphids they can produce honeydew, encouraging sooty mould, and they are important in the transmission of virus

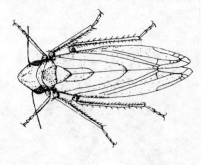

30 Leafhopper.

diseases. The nymphs commonly leave behind their skins at moulting, so they are often called 'ghost flies'. The adult hops when disturbed but will soon return to the foliage, which shows tiny bleached areas where the pest has been feeding.

Psyllids

These are commonly referred to as plant lice because they are excellent at jumping, thanks to very long hind legs. They can be separated from leafhoppers as they characteristically hold their wings almost vertical when they are at rest. Most psyllids are specific to a particular tree or shrub, and they are often responsible for galls. Galls can be likened to cancer in that a gall is an unusual growth of the plant cells,

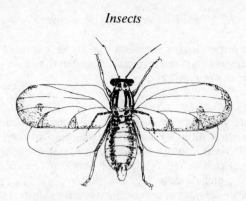

31 Psyllid – with long legs used for jumping.

stimulated by some other activity, in this case the sucking of the psyllid. The cabbage gall on box is produced by the activities of a psyllid.

Scale Insects

These insects are unlike normal insects because they are protected by a tough scale (hence the name) which is often very like the host material they are feeding on. They feed in a similar way to the other sucking

32 Scale insect merging into the stem structure.

pests, and can multiply very successfully by reproducing without mating. The scale protects the insect from predators and sprays, and may be covered in a waxy material, as with currant scale.

Mealy Bugs

These insects are very similar to scale insects but they are protected by a powdery white wax instead of a scale. They gain extra protection by hiding within curled leaves, or sheltering at the leaf base. Some mealy bugs live in the soil and feed on grass roots, but they become pests only under glasshouse conditions.

Whiteflies

Whiteflies are small, easily recognized insects. The adults look like tiny white moths, due to a powdery wax coating on their wings. They are commonly found on the undersides of leaves, but they flutter as soon as they are disturbed. The female whitefly lives for about three weeks, during which time she lays around 200 eggs. The eggs are laid in groups on the undersides of leaves, each one on a short stalk, and hatch after about ten days. The nymph is flat and scale-like, and slowly crawls around the leaf, sucking out the plant juices as it moves. As the

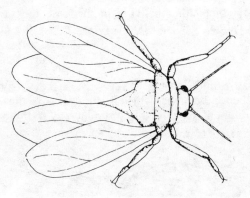

33 Adult whitefly – feeds on the underside of leaves.

nymph gets older, it develops a thicker, waxy scale and remains in one position on the leaf. Both the nymph and the adult are plant pests, mainly because they are the cause of secondary infection, either through the transmission of viruses from one plant to another or, more commonly, because whiteflies excrete a lot of honeydew and this is followed by the growth of sooty mould.

The whitefly found outdoors on cabbages is a totally different species to the one found in the sheltered glasshouse environment.

Thrips

These tiny insects should be classified in a group on their own, but as they pierce plant cells with their stylets, suck out the plant juices and are found in very large numbers, they are similar to the aphid group.

48

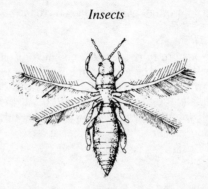

34 Thrip, or thunder fly – showing the feathery wings.

They can easily be distinguished by use of a hand lens as their wings are fringed to form feathery structures; you possibly already know them as thunder flies. They are found in many different environments, one of the commonest being among flower heads. This can produce a mottled, silvery appearance where they damage the cells, and they may transmit virus diseases. They can be beneficial by aiding pollination, and on the garden scale are rarely considered as pests.

Western flower thrips are pests which have recently caused extensive damage in a few commercial glasshouse crops. They have come from overseas and may eventually find their way all over this country. Some thrips are predacious on spider mites, so are certainly important for biological control (see Chapters 5 and 8).

Capsid Bugs

These are correctly included within the aphid group although bugs are generally larger and more complicated in structure. They feed by sucking either on plant material, in which case they are classified as pests, or on animal material, such as spider mites and leafhoppers, in which case they are certainly beneficial. This immediately produces a problem if chemicals are going to be used to control pests which suck, as beneficial capsids will be destroyed.

Damaging Capsids

The apple capsid and common green capsid larva are both pests, as they feed on the young growth of apples, pears and soft fruit. This produces brown flecking, tattered holes and distortion on the leaves and corky areas on the fruits. To avoid damage to pollinating insects, chemical control of the pest can be used only after flowering, but it needs to be carried out before the fruitlets are damaged by the insects.

Beneficial Capsids
Black-kneed capsids are fairly easy to recognize because they have a black band at the base of the long segment of each leg. The bugs are green in colour with reddish eyes. The adults lay their eggs between July and October, the female slitting the soft tissue of apple wood and burying her eggs (she may lay up to fifty all told) under the bark. The

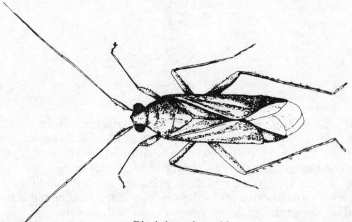

35 Black-kneed capsid.

individual eggs hatch around late spring the following year, and the nymph spends the next month or so running actively over the leaf surface and sucking at food. Red spider mite females are particularly tasty, but they also feed on other mites, leafhoppers, aphids, thrips and caterpillars.

There are many other capsids which are also found and they feed on mites, aphids and other small insects.

BUTTERFLIES AND MOTHS

Butterflies and moths are some of the easier insects to recognize, especially in the adult form, when they usually have two pairs of membranous wings covered with tiny scales. The life cycle (see Fig. 11 on page 14) shows four distinct stages; the larva or caterpillar is the feeding stage, possessing jaws for biting, mainly at plant material. The adults feed on liquid food, especially nectar, and so they are equipped with a long, hollow sucking tube or proboscis, which is curled up under the insect's head when not in use.

Butterflies and moths are commonly distinguished by their antennae. Butterflies in this part of the world have knobs at the end of their antennae. Many people think that butterflies are good and moths are bad, but this is far from the truth. There are many fewer British butterflies than moths and the commonest ones are probably the white butterflies whose larvae are so fond of cabbages. A lot of moths do have harmful larvae, but there are many others which we are rarely aware of as their larvae feed on weed plants and never cause us any harm.

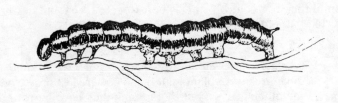

36 'Crawler' caterpillar – with five pairs of prolegs.

Larval identification can be difficult, but a recognition of larval structure will help. Many caterpillars have three pairs of legs at the head end, and also have five pairs of prolegs or props, which help them to crawl. The other caterpillars are known as 'loopers' as they have only two pairs of prolegs and move by looping the body upwards in an arch. (Do not confuse sawfly larvae with those of moths and butterflies: see page 72).

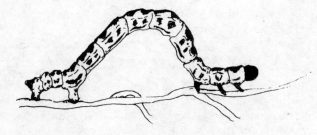

37 'Looper' caterpillar – with only two pairs of prolegs.

Leaf Webbers

Some moths cause damage because the larvae form a protective web in which they feed. They can be found on various plants but are most commonly seen on hawthorn, juniper, cotoneaster, prunus and roses. If webbing is seen early enough, it is sufficient just to destroy the web to prevent further damage.

Leaf Tiers

The main offenders here are the tortrix moths, the caterpillars of which tie together leaves with silk and then feed away in safety. This makes them difficult to control, so it is best to get in first and destroy the affected parts to prevent spread.

Leaf Eaters

There are quite a large number of species which spend their larval stage feeding directly on plant material. They are less protected than some of the other species, but by the time they have burrowed into your best cabbage, they are difficult to get at. They can do a tremendous amount of damage to crops, so you have to decide whether to use chemicals or not, and if so, to be careful to avoid killing other beneficial insects.

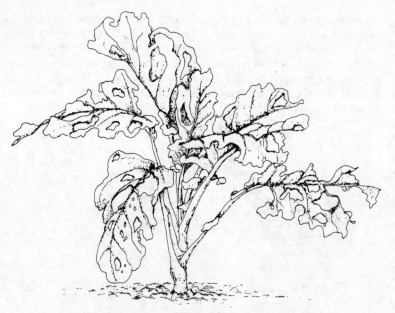

38 Cabbage plant severely damaged by caterpillars.

Stem Borers

The larvae of some moths bore into the stems of many herbaceous plants, such as foxglove and hollyhock. This may destroy the plant's vascular system, causing it to wilt and die. Others attack woody plants, but this causes only distortion and dieback. Once again, control is best effected by removing the damaged material to prevent spread.

Leaf Miners

Leaf mines are made when larvae wander through leaf tissues, separating them and producing scars. Many of the leaf miners are moths, but some are flies.

Apple and Rose Leaf Miner
The mines produced on apple and rose leaves are the result of the larva of a tiny moth. A closely related species produces the decorative mines on bramble leaves.

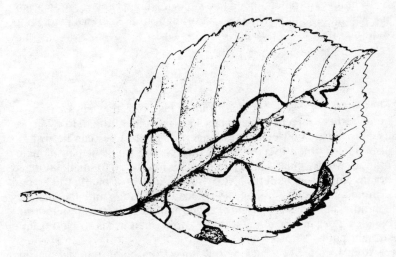

39 Mines on an apple leaf.

Privet and Lilac Leaf Miner
This is a fairly common problem. The caterpillars produce the blister type of mine, but they emerge later and roll the leaf backwards, binding it together with silk. They are found in June, with a second generation in the autumn.

Laburnum Leaf Miner

This larva tunnels into the leaf in May–June and mines a passage, but eventually settles down, producing a blotch mine and causing the whole leaf to brown and die.

Cutworms

These are the caterpillars of various moths, but the larvae are all soft, fat creatures which bite stems of plants at or just below ground level. This causes the whole plant to wilt, collapse and die, although the rest of it may be unharmed. The caterpillars, which are most active at night, spend the day hiding in the soil or among the vegetation. Most caterpillars of this group feed in July and pass through the whole life cycle rapidly, but there are others which feed over the winter. The easiest way to control cutworms is to have a tidy garden so there is nowhere for the caterpillars to hide during the day.

Swift Moths

Swift moth caterpillars spend two years feeding. They eat roots, causing wilting of plants. They can be brought to the surface by digging, and then they are a popular food for birds.

FLIES

Flies are never a very popular group of insects as they always bring to mind rather objectionable types like the bluebottle. However, as usual, a little knowledge is a dangerous thing. Flies can be distinguished from other insects because they possess only one pair of membranous wings, and the hind pair of wings is reduced to small, knobbed organs known as halteres. Next time you swot a bluebottle, spend a moment or two looking at its beautiful wings and the halteres behind. The wings are used for flight and the halteres are important balancing organs, enabling a fly to know when it has strayed from a straight path.

Adult flies feed by sucking out juice from plant material or from decaying organic matter. The larvae are very simple, usually developing in a very sheltered environment, but many of them have mouthparts constructed of hooks, which are used to tear the food material apart (see Fig. 41 on page 56). Fly larvae have no legs and move around in a worm-like fashion, but they are basically very sedentary creatures, more interested in feeding. When the larva is fully fed it pupates. Fly pupae can be in various forms, although many are encased in a tough, protective puparium. Other pupae may show some of the features of the future adult, such as a shadowing where the legs are developing, but often the pupal stage is tidily hidden away, so you are unlikely to come across it in the normal garden routine.

Fly Leaf Miners

The larvae of some flies tunnel in between the tissues of leaves, producing a line or blotch pattern on the leaves which can be quite attractive. As the larva wanders around during development, the tunnels increase in width and although they begin as a silvery pattern, they soon turn brown as more tissue is damaged.

The commonest leaf miner is the chrysanthemum leaf miner, because many people grow chrysanthemums in greenhouses and this enables five or six generations of leaf miner a year to get working. The mines are very small in the early stages and so they often escape unnoticed. Outside chrysanthemums rarely suffer any serious damage from this pest. It is the same species which causes mines on cinerarias and also weeds like the sow thistle.

Holly leaf miner is perhaps more widespread. It can be recognized by yellowish-brown blotches on the foliage, but is fairly difficult to control by means of sprays due to the size of the plant and the waxy nature of the leaves. On small plants, satisfactory control can be obtained by picking off the offending leaves and destroying them. The pupal stage is in the form of a puparium, which eventually hatches to the adult fly. Adults are about 1.5 mm (¹/₁₆ in) long and are rather like tiny black houseflies.

Rootflies

The adult flies are a dark-grey colour and are similar to houseflies. They lay their eggs in late April or May, and when the larvae hatch out, they move to the roots, feeding there for the next few weeks. They

40 Adult carrot fly and (right) damage caused by carrot fly larvae.

55

pupate in the soil, and a second generation of larvae may appear in late June. Plants attacked show poor growth; if they are small, they may collapse and die. The commonest root flies are the carrot root fly, which also attacks parsnips and parsley, and the cabbage root fly, which attacks most of the cabbage family but will also feed on aubretia, wallflowers and stocks.

Crane Flies

Crane flies or daddy longlegs are common visitors to most gardens and become household visitors in the late summer, terrifying people by fluttering past them and getting trapped in hair or clothing. No doubt the experience is as unpleasant for them!

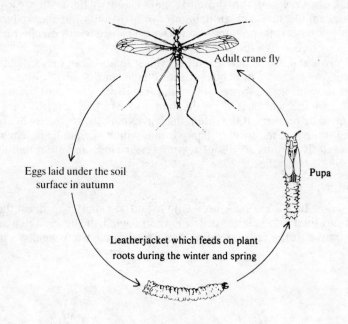

Adult crane fly

Pupa

Eggs laid under the soil
surface in autumn

Leatherjacket which feeds on plant
roots during the winter and spring

41 Crane fly life cycle.

There are several species of crane fly but only three are real pests. The adults mate in late August or September, just after they emerge from the pupa. The female lays her eggs in small groups immediately below the soil surface, especially where there is good plant cover, such as a lawn area. The eggs will hatch a couple of weeks later and the larva or leatherjacket begins to feed on the plant roots. Leatherjackets can grow to about 35 mm (1⅜ in) long. They have no legs and no distinct head, and a greyish-brown, tough, wrinkled skin. Leatherjackets require moisture, and many will be killed if it is very warm and dry soon after the larvae emerge. The larvae continue to feed throughout the winter and spring, pupating in the summer.

Leatherjackets can be controlled on a small scale by watering a lawn at night, covering it with a tarpaulin and gathering the larvae the following morning. Alternatively, insecticides can be used during mild, humid weather in autumn or spring.

Hover Flies

Hover flies are fairly easy to recognize because they remain in one position for a while, and then move on to another spot by rapidly vibrating their membranous wings. They commonly have yellow and black markings on the abdomen – a defence mechanism to confuse birds and other predators, which mistake the flies for wasps.

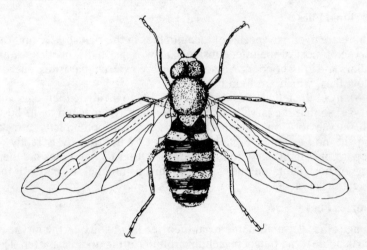

42 Hover fly.

Many hover fly larvae feed on aphids. Their eggs, which are white or yellow, are laid on leaves. The soft, legless larva emerges in a few days, and then uses the hooks around its mouth to seize aphid prey and suck up the contents. The larva holds the aphid away from the plant so it cannot escape, then pupates when it has fed enough – this may be after it has consumed several hundred or so aphids. It forms a hard, protective case known as a puparium. In some species there may be several generations a year.

Hover flies appear to be directly affected by the state of the aphid colonies, and females have been found to withhold egg-laying while there are no aphids about. When conditions are good, they lay many eggs as near as possible to the largest aphid colonies. The adult female fly needs to feed on pollen and nectar to ensure the ripening of her ovaries. The female is attracted to the aphids by scent, and is able to find aphids hidden within curled leaves or in a gall. She will lay one egg at each aphid colony. The aphids hardly appear to notice her arrival, although adult aphids tend to record her with their antennae and walk away.

Aphids are often defended from predators by ants, who appreciate the honeydew which aphids produce. The common black ant will protect the black bean aphid, but the hover fly larvae counteract the attack by producing a protective slimy exudation. Hover flies are certainly very effective predators, but their numbers have been reduced by the use of chemicals and the clearance of wilder areas.

Tachinid Flies

There are over 250 species of tachinid flies in the British Isles and the larvae of most of them feed inside earthworms, snails, beetles, caterpillars and grasshoppers. Some of them are external parasites, such as blow flies, which are found on sheep.

Many of the female tachinid flies are able to incubate their eggs and larvae, so that the larva is active as soon as it is deposited on its host. The larvae hook on to the host and absorb their food directly, attacking the non-essential organs of the host. When the fly is ready to pupate, it is then likely to kill the host. Other tachinid flies lay their eggs on host plants and the eggs do not hatch until they are eaten by the insect or larva.

Fungus Flies

Fungus flies get their name from their feeding habits, as the larvae in particular eat the fungal mycelium around rotting organic matter. The adult flies are dainty, with long antennae and extra-long back legs, which cause them to move around with a humped back. The adult flies may feed on aphids and other soft insects. Some species have become pests in a greenhouse situation, where the adults are attracted to organic fertilizers such as dried blood. The larvae are about 5 mm (1/5 in) long, with translucent bodies and black shiny heads, and they feed on young roots of seedlings and cuttings. The complete life cycle takes four to seven weeks, so the numbers can build up quickly, but most gardeners will not often have to resort to chemical control methods.

Fruit flies are often found in similar situations. They are also tiny and tend to be seen in clouds around a compost heap or, as suggested by their name, around over-ripe fruit. These flies are often used for genetics experiments, because they reproduce very rapidly. They are fairly distinctive, with red eyes, but they are not harmful.

Gall Midges

Midges are tiny flies which often pass unnoticed in the normal garden. But the larvae of the flies, which are small and maggot-like, feed within leaf tissue, and this causes the plant to produce galls on the upper surface of the leaf. The commonest ones found in Britain are those which affect chrysanthemums in the greenhouse, those which attack violets, those which attack soft fruit such as currants, and others which attack the leaves of woody plants such as willow, ash and hawthorn. The adult flies are fairly simple and often have orange-brown bodies and membranous wings with hardly any veins. The larvae are often orange also, but in most cases they do insufficient damage to require any form of control.

BEETLES

As beetles are the largest group of insects, there are many different species, both beneficial and harmful, to identify. The front wings in beetles have become toughened to form the protective elytra or case, but they still have a pair of hind wings, which many species can use for flight. They seem to prefer to stay on firm ground, so they will often be found scuttling in and out of the vegetation. Small children and entomologists alike will bury jars in the ground (referred to professionally as pitfall traps) and when the traps are inspected they will contain mainly beetles. The elytra protect the body and reduce water loss, so beetles may be found in many different habitats, the garden being no exception.

Beetle eggs are fairly simple and usually pass unnoticed as they are hidden away near a food source or scattered randomly. They hatch out to the larval form, which can be varied in type but always has a well-developed head and biting mouthparts, similar to the adult. The cockchafer larva (see Fig. 50 on page 65) is very typically C-shaped, with a brownish head, ferocious-looking jaws and three pairs of legs, which appear somewhat useless when you pick it up but enable it to move through the soil very easily. Another type of larva is more complicated to look at: the body shows the head, thorax and abdomen of a typical insect and such larvae seem more able to look after themselves; wireworms would come in this category (see Fig. 49 on page 64). The third type of beetle larva is the soft type, rather like a caterpillar. Here the ladybird larva is a good example (see Fig. 43 on this page). They can be distinguished from caterpillars as they have no false legs but just three pairs of legs on the thorax. The bark beetle is another example of the last type and is very simple, soft and unprotected, as it is always found in a sheltered spot (see Fig. 46 on page 63).

After the larval stage, the pupal stage is more uniform. The pupae show distinct legs, which can allow slight movement even though they may often be found within a protective cocoon.

Ladybirds

Ladybirds are colourful beetles to look at and are one of the few creepy-crawlies that most people find quite attractive. They are also extremely beneficial as they are predators of aphids, scale insects, mealy bugs, thrips and mites. They are beneficial all through their lives, but many people do not recognize the larval and pupal forms. More than once I have been asked if a ladybird larva was in fact that of a Colorado beetle!

As adults ladybirds spend the winter finding shelter within plant material, under bark or within houses. In the spring they emerge from

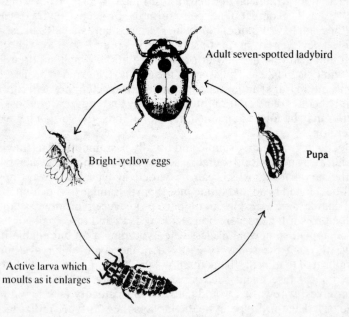

Adult seven-spotted ladybird

Pupa

Bright-yellow eggs

Active larva which
moults as it enlarges

43 Ladybird life cycle.

60

hibernation and search for suitable food material. The ladybirds mate and the female lays bright-yellow, elongate eggs in clusters, rows or individually, mainly on plant material but sometimes on stones. The eggs hatch in two days to a week and the larva emerges. The dusky-coloured larvae feed actively on other organisms and they moult three times before hatching into the plump pupal stage. The pupal skin eventually splits and the adult beetle emerges.

Ladybirds have particular likes and dislikes and the black bean aphid, for example, seems to be less nutritious than others, reducing the fertility of the ladybird. Large numbers of aphids are eaten by one ladybird larva. For instance, a seven-spotted ladybird can manage 400 greenfly in five days. When a ladybird larva attacks one member of an aphid colony, the other aphids start to kick in order to try and push away the predator. Some may even attack the ladybird with a waxy secretion which causes temporary paralysis. There are now some chemicals which will kill aphids but not harm ladybirds, and if chemical control of aphids is necessary, these are the ones that should be used.

Ground Beetles

There are over 350 species of ground beetle in Britain, and they tend to be found in soil and organic matter. A few of them are pests – for example, the strawberry ground beetle – but the majority are important both in the breakdown of organic material and as predators on other pests. The larvae of ground beetles have well-armoured, narrow bodies, and they remain in the soil or at the soil surface, because they require damp conditions. The adults can be more active: the violet ground beetle, for example, climbs trees in order to catch caterpillars of the oak tortrix moth and winter moth. Ground beetles have been

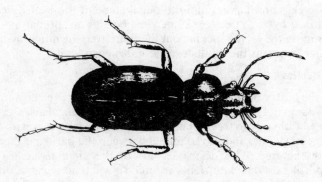

44 Ground beetle.

shown to be very important predators of the eggs of cabbage root fly – one beetle managing an average daily meal of eighteen eggs! The beetle larvae move around with open jaws and feed on slow-moving, soft animals such as earthworms and eelworms and on any animal debris.

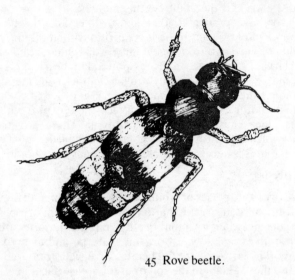

45 Rove beetle.

Rove Beetles

There are over 900 species of rove beetle in Britain. They feed on rotting plant and animal material and some are predacious. They eat root fly eggs and larvae, and the pupal stage of the root fly can be parasitized by rove beetles. Some rove beetles are predators of red spider mite, the larvae sucking out the fluid from the mites or sucking the eggs, whereas the adults eat the mites completely.

Bark Beetles

Since the horror of Dutch elm disease, bark beetles have become more widely known. Dutch elm disease is, of course, a fungal disease, but it is spread from tree to tree by beetles carrying fungal spores with them. Bark beetle adults and larvae tunnel between the bark and the living part of the tree. This destroys some of the plant tissue used for transporting food and nutrients around, so will tend to cause dieback and premature death. The female beetle bores into the bark and lays her eggs in crevices in the tunnel walls. When the larvae hatch, they

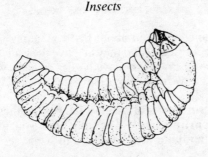

46 Simple beetle larva of the bark beetle.

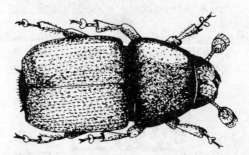

47 Adult bark beetle.

burrow away from the original tunnel, producing a typical radiating pattern. The larvae pupate in these new tunnels, emerge through the bark by tiny holes and then fly off to a new site.

Weevils

Weevils, common visitors to the garden, are fairly easy to recognize as the head is extended to form a snout with the jaws at the end and the

48 Adult weevil and (right) head showing the biting mouthparts.

elbowed antennae coming out about half-way along. There are over 500 British species of weevil and they all have these distinctive characteristics, but many of them also have bodies covered with tiny scales, and this produces attractive coloration. Adult weevils are plant pests as they bite off pieces of plant material. The larvae are legless, with curved, white, fleshy bodies and brown heads, and they tend to prefer more sheltered environments. They are found mainly in the soil, attacking roots, but quite often they are in seeds.

Click Beetles

These beetles are better known in the larval form, which is the wireworm. Wireworms are important plant pests and they should be carefully identified – many an innocent centipede has been squashed in the name of a wireworm!

Wireworms are shiny, yellow or reddish-yellow creatures, with three pairs of legs on the thorax and strong jaws at the head end. The eggs are laid between May and July, usually in moist soil where there

49 Wireworm – the active larva of the click beetle.

are plenty of fibrous roots. The larvae take about four weeks to hatch, and then spend the next four or five years feeding and growing. They are most active in spring and autumn. Once they have fed enough, they burrow deeper into the soil, usually in the summer, and pupate. Three or four weeks later they become adult, but they often hibernate until the following spring.

The adult click beetles, which are brown, elongate in shape and about 13 mm (¹⁄₁₂ in) long, produce a characteristic clicking sound when they flick themselves over after accidentally landing on their backs, hence their name.

Chafer Beetles

Cockchafer beetles, also referred to as May bugs, are about 25 mm (1 in) long, with reddish-brown wing cases. They spend the daylight hours resting on plant material, and chew leaves and plant material.

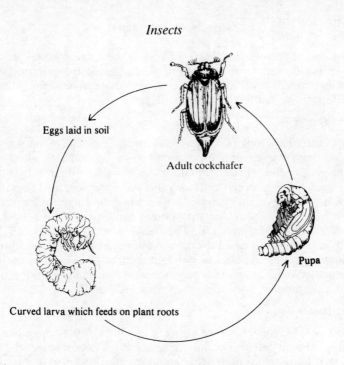

Eggs laid in soil

Adult cockchafer

Pupa

Curved larva which feeds on plant roots

50 Cockchafer beetle life cycle.

However, it is the larvae which are more destructive. The eggs are laid in the soil, and when the larvae hatch five or six weeks later, they start feeding on plant roots. They hibernate during the winter and cause extensive damage the following summer. They are fairly easy to recognize as the body is curved and the head is provided with extremely powerful jaws.

BEES AND WASPS

The main insects in this group are fairly easy to describe because the adult species have a distinct 'waist' between the thorax and abdomen, and many of them also demonstrate interesting social behaviour. The only difficult group comprises the sawflies, because they do not have a waist, but as they have two pairs of membranous wings it should be easy to separate them from flies, and they are certainly not like any other insects.

Perhaps you have already been surprised to find how many insects that you thought were pests have, in fact, a good side to them. Now we come to the bees, and I expect you feel quite convinced that the goodies are here at last. Well, of course, bees are marvellous creatures, because they provide us with so much and are so important in pollination. However, there are some bees that can be harmful to your garden, so we had better begin with them.

Leaf-Cutter Bees

Leaf-cutter bees look fairly similar to honey bees except that they are stouter and are covered in golden-brown hairs. Many shrubs are damaged by the female leaf-cutter bee, as she will cut out circular portions of leaf material and carry them away to construct the cells in which she brings up her young. Nests can be found in decaying wood or soil. Each egg is provided with honey and pollen before the cell is sealed with the leaf material. The female is most active during June and July, and the new adults do not emerge from the pupae until the following spring. These independent solitary bees may be useful in pollination of plants with very open flowers, especially members of the *Rosaceae* family.

The Honey Bee

Most people realize that we are very indebted to the honey bee, not only for honey but also because it is the activity of these insects when they visit flowers for pollen that pollinates the flowers so that fruit will form. It is fascinating to watch them feeding, and they will sting you only as a defence mechanism, not because they have anything against

51 Worker bee – with a hairy body for collecting pollen.

you! In fact, their attack is suicidal, so it is best not to annoy bees for both your sake and theirs.

The bee colony is made up of three types of individuals: the queen, whose main job is to lay eggs; the drones, which are the males who will mate with the next queen; and the workers, who are sterile females carrying out all the social duties. Most of the bees that visit flowers will be workers, and they will collect the pollen on their hairy bodies. As they leave the flower, they brush their bodies clean with their legs, and then the back pair of legs collects all the pollen together. The worker then moves on to another flower of the same sort and continues until well laden. She returns to the hive, where other workers will store the pollen in cells. When a foraging worker has found a particularly good source of food, she will return to the hive and do a dance which explains to the other bees how far away the food is, and in which direction to fly. Older workers also collect nectar, which is a dilute sugar solution produced by flowers. The bee sucks up the nectar with its straw-like tongue and mixes it with an enzyme which alters the sugar and reduces the water content. This mixture is taken to the hive, where other workers change it into honey.

The queen bee is more matronly in shape than the workers, and she spends her time laying eggs. These eggs will develop into one of the two female types of bee, depending solely upon diet. New queen bees are fed on royal jelly, workers on mere honey. Drones, which develop from an unfertilized egg, are reared from spring onwards, but at the end of the season they are not readmitted to the hive, so they will starve to death.

Bumble Bees

The life of a bumble bee is similar to that of a honey bee except that it makes its nests in holes or burrows under the ground. The mated queen bee is the only one to survive the winter, and when spring comes she emerges from hibernation and looks for somewhere to nest. She will make a wax cell and put a supply of pollen and nectar there before laying a few eggs. She will stay with the eggs, and when the young workers hatch as larvae, she will feed them so that they are fully grown within a couple of weeks. The workers take over food collection, while the queen busies herself laying more eggs. Both honey bees and bumble bees are essential for the pollination of many of our flowers.

True Wasps

True wasps are given that name to distinguish them from the digger wasps, which will be dealt with in the next section. They can be identified by their crescent-shaped eyes and the fact that they fold their wings lengthwise when they are not flying. The larvae are carnivorous, feeding on other insect larvae. Adult wasps like sweet things, but they are not equipped with the nectar-sucking equipment of butterflies and bees, so they will feed on damaged fruit and suchlike to obtain sugar.

Common wasps behave very like bumble bees, but their nests are more elaborate as they are built up of thousands of paper cells. The nest may be underground, under the eaves of buildings or anywhere similar, as long as it is sheltered. The queen wasp scrapes off thin fragments of wood using her strong jaws. She macerates the wood and, as it mixes with her saliva, it produces a pulpy mixture. She makes a foundation, then returns to get more building materials. Once she has produced a small, rounded structure with a few individual cells in it, she lays some eggs. She continues building until the eggs hatch into larvae, and then she has to find aphids and caterpillars to feed the larvae. When the workers emerge, they take over the job of nest-building, and feeding future larvae, while the queen spends her time laying more eggs. New queens will develop and mate before finding a dry corner to hibernate in, but all the other wasps die as the temperature begins to drop.

Digger Wasps

These are solitary wasps which keep their wings flat over their bodies when they are resting. They dig their nests in soil or rotten wood. They certainly should not be killed, as they feed on insects, including aphids.

Ichneumon Flies

These are really incorrectly named as they are not flies but another type of wasp. There are over 1,800 identified species, and the majority

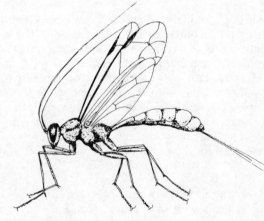

52 Ichneumon – showing long antennae and large ovipositor.

of the larvae are parasitic on the larvae of the caterpillars of butterflies and moths. The adults have long antennae which are constantly in motion as the insect seeks for a likely food source. Female ichneumons often have a very obvious ovipositor, and it is with this that the parasitism begins. Once the adult female finds a suitable host, using her antennae as a guide, she arches her body, pierces the host body with her ovipositor and lays her eggs inside. When the eggs hatch into the larval form, the larva feeds from the host's tissue, but initially this only reduces the host activity and does not kill it. When the larvae are fully grown, they eventually kill the host, and this is closely followed by pupation.

Braconids

Braconids are very similar insects to ichneumon flies, the main differences being found in the patterning of the veins of the wings. The particularly important one is a common parasite of cabbage white butterfly caterpillars. Each caterpillar may be host to over 100 larvae, which kill the caterpillar just before they pupate. They produce bright-yellow cocoons on the collapsed skin of the caterpillar. These should be left to allow the predator to complete its life cycle, and hopefully control future generations of caterpillars.

Another braconid parasitizes greenfly, while another attacks the carrot fly.

Chalcid Wasps

These are common insects and there are hundreds of different species found in Britain. They are usually less than 3 mm (⅛ in) long but they

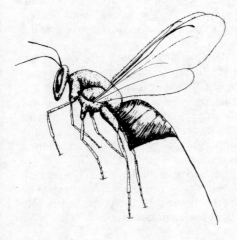

53 Chalcid wasp – with elbowed antennae and simple veins.

can be extremely beautiful, with blue or green metallic sheens to their bodies. Most of them parasitize the young stages of many other insects, and they have been used successfully in biological control programmes (see p. 96). The most important features for recognition are the elbowed antennae and the wings, which have very simple venation and so are quite distinctive.

One chalcid wasp, *Encarsia formosa*, has been used very successfully in the biological control of glasshouse whitefly. If you have a greenhouse or grow curly kale in the garden, you have probably come across whitefly (see page 48). The scale stage of the whitefly makes it fairly safe from chemical attack, but the chalcid wasp lays her egg in a whitefly scale. The larva develops, causing the scale to turn black, and the adult chalcid cuts its way out of the scale about one month later. The chalcid wasp reproduces mainly without mating, and if she cannot find a suitable scale to lay her egg in, she may 'sting' and kill older whitefly.

The wasp needs the whitefly to complete her life cycle, so if this is a method of control, it is necessary to have slightly more prey than predators, otherwise the predator will die out once all the whitefly have been controlled. However, the numbers of whitefly needed to satisfy the chalcid wasp are not sufficient to cause severe damage to plants.

Cynipid Wasps

These are the wasps which produce many of the galls which are commonly found on oak trees. Oak apple galls are produced when the female cynipid wasp deposits her eggs at the base of a bud. This causes the bud to swell and by June or July it is fully developed. The adults emerge and, after mating, lay their eggs in small roots in the soil. Another smaller gall is then produced. In the spring about sixteen months later, wingless female wasps emerge, crawl up the tree and the cycle begins once more.

Spangle galls on oak leaves demonstrate another case where two different generations complete the life cycle. Inside the spangle galls the larvae feed and grow and eventually separate from their host in the autumn. They continue to develop and pupate during the winter, female wasps emerging the following spring. These lay their unfertilized eggs on male catkins or young leaves, and they produce small currant-like galls. In May–June the adults hatch and, after mating, they will produce spangle galls once more.

Robin's pincushion is a condition also produced by the cynipid wasp. This is caused by the female laying her eggs in unopened rosebuds. The plant produces a ball of moss-like tissue which is usually brightly coloured. Inside there is a mass of individual chambers where the larvae develop, remaining within the gall until the adults emerge the following spring and the cycle is repeated.

None of these galls is particularly harmful to the plant, but they can be interesting to watch, and other insects may also make use of the galls as a protective home. Many cynipid wasps are also parasites of insect larvae.

Ants

Ants show the characteristic feature of this group as their body has a definite 'waist'. Ants are usually wingless but at certain times of the year winged forms develop and a mating flight follows. Several species of ant are commonly found in gardens, making their nests in soil, under stones or paving or in old tree stumps. Most of you will have met ants when you've been in the garden, and may have been shocked by a bite from their powerful jaws. Some of them sting, but many defend themselves by squirting formic acid at their enemies.

Ants are social insects, living in a colony with a queen ant, male ants and worker ants. The mating flight usually takes place in August, and the male and female mate in flight. The fertilized queen lands and bites off her own wings, and then she digs a hole and lays a batch of eggs. She feeds these ants and they are the first workers who will take on the job of looking after the colony. The queen ant spends the rest of her time laying eggs, which are taken away by the workers and tended elsewhere. The larvae are fed on honey and insect grubs.

Ants are very fond of sweet materials and they are often found near aphid colonies as they feed on the honeydew produced by the aphids. Some species can be observed 'milking' the aphids – stroking the aphid with their antennae which stimulates the production of honeydew. Sometimes they tend a certain colony of aphids, and shelter the aphids from fungi and other predators, and others are known to keep aphid eggs in their nest during the winter, returning the aphid nymphs to plant material in spring.

Most householders think ants are dreadful organisms, but in the garden, unless their nest is built just beneath a plant, they rarely cause much damage. They feed their larvae on other organisms and aid in the aeration of soil and the mixing up of different layers of soil. The wood ant collects much plant material to furnish its nest, and this is gradually converted to organic matter in the soil.

Sawflies

Sawflies belong to the same group as the ants, bees and wasps but they lack the distinctive waist. They get their name from the ovipositor, because it is toothed like a saw and is used to cut slits in plant material before the female deposits her eggs. The wood wasp can penetrate

71

54 Adult sawfly and (right) sawfly larva, distinguished by the prolegs along the posterior segments.

wood with her sharp ovipositor. When the eggs hatch, the sawfly larvae which emerge are similar to caterpillars but they have stumpy prolegs all along their soft abdomens. They are pests at this stage as they feed on plant material.

The commonest examples which are found in the garden are the rose, gooseberry, birch and Solomon's seal sawflies. The larvae are highly decorated, with spots on their coloured bodies, and they frequently demolish large areas of leaves, starting at the outer edge and maybe almost entirely defoliating the plant.

Another sawfly is the leaf-rolling rose sawfly. This leaf-rolling is the result of the female cutting the leaf longitudinally with her ovipositor, and this causes the leaf to curl tightly around the egg. When the larvae emerge, they feed on the leaf margin and work their way out.

Slug sawflies are also found. The larvae are very slug-like to look at and are referred to as slugworms. The damage they do is distinctive, as once the larvae hatch they move to the upper surface of the leaf, where they feed by removing the upper layer of green tissue but leaving behind the veins and lower tissue. The characteristic damage is referred to as window-paning.

OTHERS

There are many other groups of insects which have not been mentioned in this book because they are less significant for the average garden, but there are a few insects which must be included because they are frequent inhabitants of the garden. You should not find them hard to recognize, and they are worth getting to know.

Lacewings

Lacewings are distinguished from other insects by the presence of delicate, membranous wings with an elaborate network of veins, and they also have very long antennae. Their bodies are usually brown or

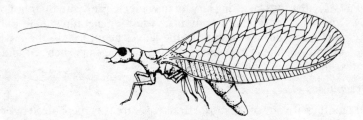

55 Adult lacewing.

green in colour. They undergo complete metamorphosis, the egg hatching into an active larva with three pairs of slender legs and curved, hollow jaws, which they use to catch other insects and suck out the body contents. The pupal stage is passed inside a silk cocoon.

Green Lacewings
These are often found in houses as they are attracted to the light. They have bright-green bodies, green-veined wings and a yellow, metallic glow to their compound eyes. They fly slowly, and produce an unpleasant odour when they are handled. The green eggs are laid on stalks on a leaf surface. The larvae hatch and feed on aphids, leafhoppers and other small, soft-bodied insects. They may camouflage themselves by covering their backs with empty aphid skins. One larva is able to eat several hundred aphids during a fortnight, so that the larva can easily influence an aphid population.

Brown Lacewings
These are smaller insects, with brown or greyish wings. The larvae feed on aphids, thrips and mites, but do not protect themselves with the skins of dead animals.

Powdery Lacewings
Powdery Lacewings are small, fragile insects with wings less veined. Their bodies and wings are covered with a white, powdery substance. The adults look rather similar to whitefly, but when they are not flying they hold their wings in a steep, arched position – rather than moth-like, as whitefly do. The eggs are very tiny, salmon-pink in colour, and

are laid on the lower surfaces of leaves or sheltered in crevices in the bark. After laying each egg, the female covers it with some of the white, powdery material which covers her body. The plump larvae are almost colourless when they hatch, but they have conspicuous red eyes. They feed mainly on mites, and while they feed they attach themselves to the leaf by secreting a sticky substance from their abdomen. As with other lacewing larvae, they pierce prey with their hollow jaws and suck out the body contents. Adult female mites seem to be the most juicy, but in autumn, as the leaves begin to fall, the larvae feed mainly on mite eggs (which are the usual stage in which red spider mites survive the winter months).

Dragonflies

Dragonflies are one of the most attractive and easily recognized insects to be found. They have long, slender bodies, large compound eyes and two pairs of delicate wings with a complex system of veins. They can have the most beautiful colours, and as they are beneficial insects, they need to be encouraged in every way possible.

The dragonfly nymph spends its life in water, so dragonflies are encouraged by ponds, rivers or nearby lakes. Adult dragonflies love the sun and can fly well, so they can be found some distance from

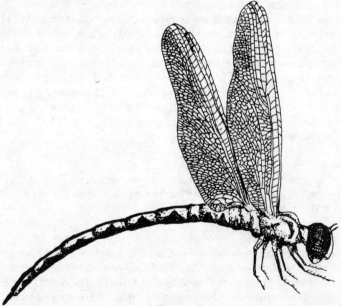

56 Dragonfly.

water. The large eyes enable them to catch their prey while on the move, and they are extremely partial to mosquitoes and flies, as well as beetles and wasps.

Mating dragonflies are a fairly common sight if you sit near ponds and streams in spring. The male searches for a female and, when he finds her, he holds her by the neck using the 'claspers' at the end of his abdomen. The female curves her body under the male until her abdomen is able to collect the sperm. The two may fly around together for quite some time. The eggs are dropped into water or laid in slits in the stems of water plants.

The nymphs have long bodies, three pairs of legs, large compound eyes and a specially modified lower jaw. This is a long, limb-like structure with two ferocious-looking hooks on the end, but it has a hinge-like joint half-way along so the larva can hide the weapon close to its head. When it sees some suitable prey, such as nymphs of other aquatic insects or even tadpoles or small fish, it shoots out this lower jaw, catching its prey and enjoying another meal.

Earwigs

Earwigs are well-known insects but only two species are common in the garden. They have long bodies which are usually a shiny chestnut-brown colour, wings tightly folded so they are seen only on closer inspection, and two large claspers at the end of the abdomen. The name 'earwig' comes from the belief that as they like hunting out dark, sheltered corners, they might also like hiding in our ears and using their claspers to give them an unpleasant pinch! This idea does not seem to have any foundation, but maybe a reader has some evidence.

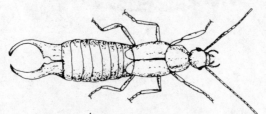

57 Earwig – with large claspers.

Earwigs shelter in the soil as winter approaches and will mate there. The female lays her eggs in an earthen cell, looking after them with loving care, regularly licking them clean to prevent attack by mildew. The young hatch in February or March, but remain with the mother until they are almost mature ten weeks later. There is commonly a second family later in the year.

Earwigs are omnivorous insects, so they can feed on insect pests such as aphids, but their choice of food is closely related to the fact that they feed at night and also that they need to be hemmed in by their surroundings. Chrysanthemum and dahlia flowers satisfy this need. If you grow these plants, you will probably have been saddened to find the flowers distorted or even prevented from opening; a sharp shake of open flowers will dislodge the pest. Trapping can be a fairly successful method of control. It is usual to use an upturned pot on the end of a cane, filling the pot with loose straw – an ideal daytime retreat!

In most cases, gardeners are able to leave earwigs to their own devices. If no harm is apparent, it is more likely that they are being helpful.

Bush Crickets

I was not going to mention bush crickets, because I tend to think of them more as creatures of the countryside, but one was hopping around my garden the other day, so he obviously felt he should be included. Bush crickets can be distinguished from grasshoppers, because they have much longer antennae. Attractive creatures to look at,

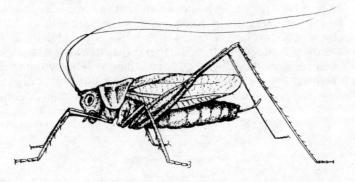

58 Bush cricket.

they may surprise you when they jump, but they seem to find crawling involves less effort. They are beneficial, because their diet includes pests such as aphids and other small insects, but as they hide during the daylight hours, you may rarely come across them.

House crickets stray into sheds and greenhouses, where they will happily feed on rubbish, but they may spread to plant material if nothing else is available.

MICROSCOPIC ORGANISMS

Many of the insects and mites which have been described are very tiny and can be studied properly only by using a lens or a microscope, but there are also many organisms which are even smaller. The majority of the microscopic organisms in the garden are beneficial, but there are some which cause our plants to suffer from diseases, and yet others can cause diseases in the pests. This is one of the ways now being investigated as a method of pest control.

ALGAE

Algae are simple plants, of which seaweed is perhaps the best known. You may have some seaweed in your garden to forecast the weather, or you may use various seaweed extracts as fertilizers, but it is the microscopic algae we are going to consider here. The majority of algae in a normal garden will be present in the soil and puddles, but algae will also be found in ponds, on paths and on the damp sides of tree trunks.

Soil algae are simple species which occur as single-celled individuals, simple filaments or colonies of simple organisms. Many of them are protected by a gummy material, although the diatoms have elaborately sculptured silicate cell walls. Many of these algae are found in the upper soil surface where some light is able to penetrate, and they will photosynthesize, building up sugars from carbon dioxide and water. Some algae live deeper in the soil and may be able to feed on organic matter.

Algae flourish on damp, sunny soils in spring and autumn, especially where the soil is fairly alkaline and fertile. They will add organic matter to a soil and help bind soil particles together, and some species also feed on atmospheric nitrogen to make their own protein, which will improve soil fertility.

Algae in puddles and on tree trunks are not particularly harmful except if you find them unpleasant. They will produce a habitat for protozoa and bacteria. Pond algae are essential for aerating the pond to keep the water fresh and provide the fish with oxygen. Some algae multiply so rapidly that they can choke a pond and they must be removed – but they can, of course, be added to the compost heap.

BACTERIA

Bacteria are the types of organism which are often maligned as they are commonly associated with 'germs', but in fact it would be true to say that without bacteria the world would be a difficult place in which to live. Our own digestive systems, for example, depend upon bacteria, and the gardener's world is a similar bacterial paradise. Yes, there are still some harmful bacteria which cause disease, but these are far less common than the beneficial varieties.

Bacterial diseases in plants tend to cause cells to collapse and break down, which often leads to a bacterial slime. Bacteria have to enter the plant by some means, so they are commonly the cause of a secondary infection where the plant has already been wounded. If you take cuttings, the wounded stem is prone to fungal and bacterial attack; to guard against this, you will find that rooting hormones often contain an additional antiseptic material. Probably the most important bacterial diseases are the bacterial wilts, which include fireblight, and the bacterial galls.

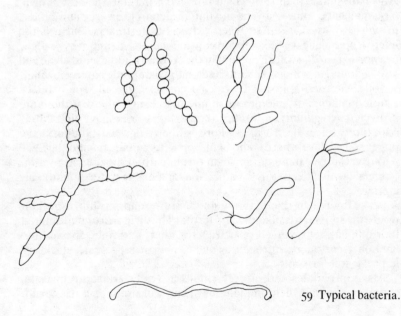

59 Typical bacteria.

78

Bacteria vary in shape but there are three basic forms: the spherical ones or cocci, which are about 1μ ($1\mu = 0.001$ mm or $1/25000$ in) in diameter; the rods or bacilli, which can be up to 10μ in length; and the spiral or spirilla, which can be up to 50μ long. They are simple, unicellular organisms which reproduce by binary fission, one organism dividing into two when the environmental conditions are ideal.

Beneficial bacteria are very important in the normal garden and they tend to be found in two habitats: the soil and the compost heap. A single gram of soil may contain over 1,000 million bacteria and these will all be active in maintaining a living soil. The commonest soil bacteria are rod-shaped and many of them can swim by means of a flagella or whip. A lot of them are protected by a chemical sheath. This may prevent the bacterium being eaten by protozoa, but it also helps bind soil particles together.

Bacteria do not contain chlorophyll, so they are unable to photosynthesize as plants do, but many of them can obtain their food from chemical sources, and they are then known as autotrophic bacteria. These bacteria are very important to the soil. The other bacteria feed on organic materials, such as rotting leaves or animal material, and by this they not only release nutrients to the soil but also improve the soil structure.

The Nitrogen Cycle

The nitrogen cycle is probably one of the best-known ways in which bacteria are shown to be of great importance. There are, however, many misconceptions about the nitrogen cycle, the most common being that peas, beans and clover are an essential part of the process. Leguminous plants are very important, but the nitrogen cycle occurs even when they are absent, so there is no need for you to turn your lawn into a clover ley!

Nitrogen is an essential element for the manufacture of protein in plants and animals, and animals obtain their nitrogen directly or indirectly from plants. Plants take up nitrogen from the soil in the form of nitrates, and they get these nitrates mainly by the activity of bacteria. If you want to give plants an extra boost, you can provide them with a nitrate fertilizer, but if it rains this will mainly find its way into the drainage system and encourage the water plants in canals and rivers. You could instead provide your plants with an ammonium fertilizer, or some form of compost which is broken down by saprophytic bacteria (those which feed on dead material) to produce ammonia. In this case other bacteria known as nitrifying bacteria come into action and convert ammonia and nitrites into the important nitrates.

Nitrogen-fixing bacteria are the ones which feed on nitrogen gas in the soil air and change this into their own body protein. They are found free-living in a healthy soil, and then others live in the lumps or nodules on the roots of leguminous plants. The nitrogen is not released as nitrates until the bacteria themselves are broken down by other bacteria. This is why it is important to leave your bean plants in the soil to allow the nitrogen to be released.

Unfortunately, there are some detrimental bacteria which break down nitrates into toxic nitrites or back into nitrogen gas. They are particularly prevalent in waterlogged soils, so it is best to encourage the beneficial bacteria by providing a well-aerated soil; and then you should not be troubled by these denitrifying bacteria. If large supplies of unrotted organic matter are added to a soil, all micro-organisms will flourish. This depletes the air in the soil and harmful bacteria will use up the nitrates.

The Carbon Cycle

Carbon is one of the basic constituents of living things and it enters the living world directly or indirectly by photosynthesis in plants or chemosynthesis in certain bacteria. This carbon is the main energy source for plants and animals, and our machines in the form of fossil fuels. If organisms die and rot down to become humus, bacteria are important in the breakdown of both organic material to produce humus and the humus to release nutrients into the soil and return the carbon dioxide to the air.

Carbon to Nitrogen Ratio

Most gardeners build a compost heap to encourage the breakdown of organic matter into beneficial humus. If you are tempted to apply the organic matter too soon, it will, as we have just said, encourage harmful bacteria and reduce the available nutrients in the soil. The reason for this is that the bacteria combine the carbon with nitrates to make new bacteria, and bacterial protein contains much more nitrogen than plant protein. So when the bacteria break up plant material, they will take nitrogen from the soil. They also use calcium to make new cell walls and this will make a soil more acid. When you make a compost heap, it is advisable to add some form of calcium or lime, and to wait until it is well rotted before adding it to the soil.

The Sulphur Cycle

Sulphur is another essential nutrient for protein synthesis and if there is plenty of air in the soil, the organic sulphur compounds produced when organisms die will be acted upon by bacteria and changed via hydrogen sulphide into sulphates. Plants take up sulphates, so the cycle is completed.

If the soil is waterlogged, certain anaerobic bacteria (they can breathe without oxygen) will abound and hydrogen sulphide will tend to accumulate, producing the characteristic 'bad egg' smell.

Bacterial 'Fertilizers'

Bacteria can be added to soils with fertilizers to increase the effectiveness of the nutrients provided, and release these nutrients to plants. This method has been used in Soviet farming for many years, and can increase plant yields. It is now possible to buy bacterial supplies to add to your compost heap, to hasten breakdown to humus, which you can safely add to your soil. Alternatively, the addition of living soil will add many natural bacteria, and they will soon flourish when surrounded by the wealth of food material.

Bacterial Diseases

Some bacteria are harmful because they use living plants as their food sources. This means they digest living tissue to absorb the nutrients from it and the result is often a slimy mess. As bacteria are such tiny and simple organisms, they often enter plants which have already been wounded, thus causing a secondary infection. They multiply most rapidly when conditions are warm and damp. Methods of controlling bacterial diseases chemically are seldom very satisfactory, and careful sanitation is essential to avoid infection wherever possible.

Bacterial diseases may cause disfigurement (such as bacterial leaf spots) but these do not cause much harm. The really damaging diseases are the ones that cause the plant to rot and wilt, often just around ground level, where the environment is more conducive to bacterial growth. Fireblight is probably the most economically important disease as it is very damaging to apples and pears and can be disastrous when it spreads through our commercial orchards. This particular infection enters the plant through the blossoms, and then moves inside the tree to spread to other branches. Whole branches will die, giving the impression of fire damage. It produces a reddish stain just below the bark, and in the early stages it may be satisfactory simply to prune off the infected material and burn it. The Fireblight Disease Order 1958 requires any suspected case to be reported to the Ministry of Agriculture, Fisheries and Food, although the disease is now so widespread that they rarely require gardeners to destroy their plants.

Bacterial Cankers
Cankers can be produced by bacteria and one type is found on cherry and plum trees. It shows up as a sticky bacterial ooze on the bark in spring and as leaf spots, with a yellow ring surrounding brown tissue, often followed by a 'shot hole' (that is to say, the dead tissue drops out). Branches may show dieback or buds may fail to break.

60 Bacterial gall on forsythia.

When cankers are formed on herbaceous plants, the leaves tend to discolour and wilt, and the stem becomes stained internally. The material collapses, but there is no evidence of mycelium (the feeding tissue) or sporing structures, as with a fungus.

Crown gall is the general name for a type of gall produced by bacteria on many different types of plant. The gall may be quite variable too, ranging from a massive distortion – as seen with the large lumps on the side of elderly tree trunks – to quite tiny lumps at the early stages. On herbaceous plants the gall or growth develops on the stem close to or just below soil level, but galls can be found elsewhere on the plant. The bacteria enter the plant through wounds, and can remain in the soil while susceptible plants are present.

PROTOZOA

Protozoa are single-celled, microscopic animals which need moisture to live in. They are present in the garden in water butts, ponds and puddles, but their most frequent habitat is the soil. Here they play an essential part in the general soil ecosystem, especially because of their feeding habits. Many protozoa feed on bacteria and will control bacterial populations; some feed on other protozoa. Soil protozoa are smaller than most water species as they are restricted to water held in the soil pores. Most of them can form cysts when conditions are particularly dry, but they return to their normal state when there is sufficient moisture.

82

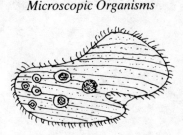

61 A protozoon which swims in soil moisture.

FUNGI

Fungi are usually described as plants even though they do not contain green chlorophyll and so have to obtain their food by feeding either parasitically on other living things or saprophytically on dead material. The parasitic fungi tend to produce disease symptoms whereas the saprophytes are normally beneficial. In the garden evidence of fungi tends to be restricted to those examples that produce large toadstool-like fruiting bodies or disease symptoms like mildew or black spot.

Beneficial Fungi
The most important fungi are found in the soil as saprophytes, feeding on organic matter and breaking it down to simpler substances. Fungi are more prevalent in soils rich in organic matter and they will be common occupants of the compost heap. They are tolerant of a wide range of pH and will be more active in acid soils as bacteria are less active there and so competition will be reduced. Many of the most simple fungi feed mainly on sugars and easily decomposable organic matter. They will often depend upon other organisms such as worms to break up the material and make it easier for the fungal mycelium to enter. Soils contain many different fungal spores which are waiting for a suitable food source.

Some of the larger fungi are able to feed on cellulose, a fibrous material, and lignin, which is the basic constituent of wood. These fungi may grow quite slowly, but they are very important, being the only organisms involved in lignin breakdown. It is not normally necessary to encourage fungi in the garden. There are always millions of tiny spores floating around in the air or water and if they land upon your compost heap or some other organic matter, they will soon set to work, utilizing the food source. But it is important to remember that fungicides are designed to kill fungi, and unwise use of soil sterilants may destroy some of the beneficial fungi, leaving you worse off than before.

62 Fungi – feeding on organic matter.

Harmful Fungi

Harmful fungi are probably the ones you have come across and it is
these that give the remainder a bad name. Garden plants are susceptible to fungal diseases, just as animals are, and some of these diseases
can cripple a plant to such an extent that it seems kindest to destroy it.
This is essential, because while you have a diseased plant around, the
trouble may spread to healthy plants. Fungal diseases often do not
show until the fungus-feeding tissue has spread throughout the plant,
and by then control methods will be costly and not always effective
anyway.

As I have done for other pests and predators in previous chapters, I
will reduce the fungal diseases to similar groups, using examples you
will have come across.

Mildews
There are two types of mildew: the powdery mildews, which grow on the outside of the plant and send in special 'roots' to extract nutrients from the plant; and the downy mildews, which grow 'down' inside the plant. In the early stages of infection, it is often possible to rub off the powdery mildews, and they are never as damaging as downy mildews, but even so the upper surfaces of leaves may often be completely white. Powdery mildew is more common when plants are overcrowded and the soil is dry. Downy mildew is seen first as a yellowing of the leaf surface, while the lower surface shows a greyish mould which is usually the reproductive spores.

Rusts
Rusts are another common group of fungal diseases, and they are aptly named as the infection shows up as bright-orange or brown pustules. There are many different rust diseases, but on the whole they are host-specific, which means the infection will not spread to a different

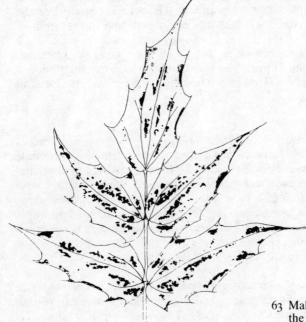

63 Mahonia rust causes the leaves to bronze.

species. The main garden plants affected are antirrhinum, hollyhock, pelargonium, chrysanthemum, mahonia, leeks, onions, mint and asparagus. If plants are particularly badly infected with rust, it is probably best to destroy the plant material and, if possible, avoid these plants for the next couple of years as these fungi survive only on living material.

Leaf Spots

The third type of disease caused by fungi are the leaf spots. These can vary from black spot on roses (a fungal infection which is common when the air is unpolluted – does that cheer you up if your roses are covered with black spot?) to leaf spots on rhododendrons, lupins, phlox and laurels. On some occasions, the infected plant material dies and drops out of the leaf. This leaves behind a hole, but it does often reduce infection.

Cankers

Cankers are local diseases found most especially on woody plants where the infected tissue distorts, dries and then splits open, exposing the living plant tissue underneath. Cankers can be produced by bacterial, mechanical damage and woolly aphid, but the commonest garden canker, found on apple and pear trees, is the result of a fungal infection. The canker can be identified if it is looked at closely because when it is active, there will be white pustules during spring, summer and autumn, or tiny bright-red lumps over the winter months. Both pustules and lumps produce spores which can spread the infection. Infection has to enter through a wound, but although careful pruning is advised, leaf scars are always open to infection for at least twenty-four hours after leaf fall.

Peach Leaf Curl

Peach leaf curl is a rather attractive-looking fungal infection of peaches and almonds. The disease causes a plant reaction: the leaves become very distorted and bright-red in colour. They are likely to fall prematurely and the infection will reduce plant growth. If possible, it is wise to remove the affected leaves before they get to the blistery stage, which is when the spores are being formed, but if a fungicidal spray is necessary, this should be used in early spring, before the buds begin to burst.

Honey Fungus

Honey fungus is one of our biggest problem fungi as it is one that can live on dead and living tissue, and while feeding on some rotting material, it can attack a healthy plant. The range of plants affected is huge, although some, such as privet, are especially susceptible; it seems to be most serious with trees and shrubs. It produces honey-coloured toadstools to distribute its spores but also spreads many metres through the soil by tough black strings of tissue, commonly referred to as 'boot laces'. Control methods are not very effective, so I hope your plants are never troubled by this disease.

Plant Wilting
The last group of fungal diseases I feel I ought to mention is the one that affects the transport system of the plant and produces wilting. Quite often the plant is damaged at soil level, where the soil is moist. The fungi are inconspicuous until severe damage has been done; plants often appear to be wilted during the day but recover in the cool of the evening, but later the lower leaves dry and eventually the plant dies.

There is also a set of diseases which attacks seeds, seedlings and newly rooted cuttings, and will also cause wilts at some stage in the proceedings as they interfere with water uptake. They flourish in the humid atmosphere required for propagation, and need to be watched for at frequent intervals so that a control method can be carried out if necessary. With a small infection it is often enough just to remove and destroy the infected material.

MYCORRHIZA

Mycorrhiza are the fungal associations found between fungi and the roots of higher plants. When these associations were first discovered, it was thought that such relationships were limited to only a few plant species, but recent work has shown that they are much more common than was first believed and had just gone unnoticed. It is easy for us to concentrate on bad things and fail to acknowledge where beneficial organisms exist.

There are two basic types of mycorrhiza: the endotrophic mycor-rhiza, where the fungus grows among the cells of the root of the higher plant; and ectotrophic mycorrhiza, where the fungus is more like a sheath of tissue on the outside of the root. In both cases the fungus soon becomes brown and muddy and may be difficult to distinguish from the root, except by sectioning the tissue and using a microscope, although the roots colonized by ectotrophic mycorrhiza tend to be very short and stubby. Heathers and orchids require mycorrhizal rela-tionships to enable the plants to grow properly, but here the fungal tissue is internal.

This association is commonly referred to as symbiotic: in other words, both the fungus and the plant benefit from the relationship. The fungus needs the plant as a home and seems unable to live separated from the root system of a plant. The plants show much better growth where there is a mycorrhizal association, and this seems to be mainly because the fungus helps the plant absorb essential nutrients from the soil. If fertilizers or manures are added to the soil, we expect to see better growth, but sometimes the results are not as dramatic as expected. This could be because the conditions are wrong for the bacteria which help in the chemical changes (see page 79); or it could be because the soil is too acid or alkaline and the nutrients have become insoluble; or again, it could be that the plant roots are not very efficient at taking up nutrients.

One of the most essential nutrients for plant growth is phosphorus, but it is also one of the most difficult to take up. Mycorrhiza seem to increase phosphorus uptake dramatically and although the process is not understood properly, this may be because the fungus increases the surface area for absorption. Such associations seem most beneficial when the soil is fairly low in nutrients.

VIRUSES

Viruses should really be considered in a separate chapter as they are defined as submicroscopic, being too small to be seen with an ordinary light microscope. They can be registered only with an electron microscope. An electron microscope works by passing a beam of electrons through the material: if an electron hits something, it will be recorded, and in this way an impression of the object can be built up. Virus particles can thus be 'observed', but it is easy enough to see evidence of many viruses and their effects on plants.

The virus particle is like a part of a cell. Some scientists believe that viruses are not living but are simply chemicals. Living or not, they are

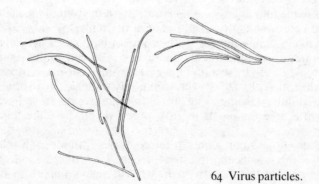

64 Virus particles.

able to multiply within living tissue and this usually produces disease symptoms. However, they are unable to move from one plant to another except with the help of a vector, and other organisms, especially insects, are important for this purpose.

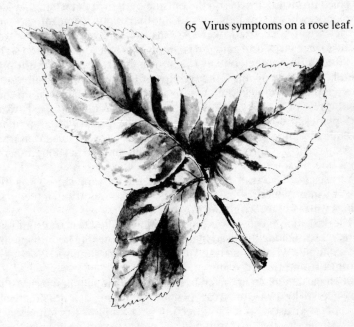

65 Virus symptoms on a rose leaf.

Symptoms

The typical symptoms which are produced often show up in the leaves first, if this is where the virus entered the plant. Mosaics or mottles are very common symptoms, once the virus has caused the chlorophyll or green colouring to break down, exposing the yellow pigments instead. This may be very distinctive, producing an attractive variegated leaf or a ring spot, which is a ring of yellowed tissue. The other main effect of viruses is to cause stunting and distortion, because the virus uses up materials the plant needed for normal growth.

Virus symptoms may often be masked during the summer months as the better growing conditions tend to overshadow any viral inhibition. Some plants, especially many of the common weeds, such as groundsel, are known to carry a latent virus infection; the virus is present in the plant itself and can spread to other plants but has no apparent effect on the host.

Spread of Viruses

Virus transmission is dependent upon a carrier or vector, many of which are insects. Winged aphids are especially important here as they will pick up virus particles on the outside of their stylet when they suck at plants; when they move on to another plant, some of the virus particles will be carried over. Aphids are known as non-persistent vectors since virus transmission is simply due to a contaminated stylet, and if they do not feed on any other virus-infected material, they will soon be harmless again. Other groups of pests are more troublesome as once they have picked up a virus infection, it remains within them for the rest of their lives. Again the trouble occurs with pests which suck plant sap, so the offending groups are the thrips, whiteflies, mealy bugs, leafhoppers and mites. Nematodes are very important in transmission of viruses through the soil, and they can also harbour infection from one season to the next.

Viruses are also transmitted when plants growing closely together become intertwined so that plant tissues get wounded and infected sap comes into contact with a healthy plant.

The last main vectors are human beings. They can transmit plant viruses by touching diseased plants and then touching healthy plants – for example, when removing side shoots from tomatoes, or taking cuttings from infected material.

Most gardeners do not need to identify individual plant viruses, but they need to be aware of virus types and symptoms. It is not practical to cure plant viruses, so if the infection gets a hold, it is important to destroy the infected material and to try to prevent vectors from carrying the infection elsewhere. It is also worth discovering if the virus in question is liable to infect other plants – we have already seen how some viruses are host-specific, which means they will infect only one plant species and will not spread all round the garden.

Insect Viruses

Many butterflies, moths, flies, beetles and wasps are known to suffer from virus diseases during their larval stages. These have occurred naturally and have effected a 'biological control' on what might otherwise have been severe pest damage. The same principle has been used as a method of insect control on lucerne; the diseased caterpillar shrivels up but remains infective to its companions. Another virus has been found which affects cabbage caterpillars, causing the larvae to burst and spread the infected body contents over the plant and soil. The uninfected caterpillars are tempted to eat the dead remains of

their brothers and sisters and this also encourages spread. This seems
an attractive proposition as a method of control for the future, as this
virus is specific to the pest and leaves no residues harmful to human
beings.

CONTROL

ECOSYSTEM

By the time you get to this chapter, assuming you have at least dipped into the previous seven, you must be beginning to realize that our gardens are full of living organisms, many of which go completely unnoticed, and many of which are extremely useful. I hope you have been stimulated to look a little more closely at some of these organisms, and maybe you have also decided that it is wise to make use of the beneficial ones. Some of the organisms are both beneficial and harmful, feeding on our pests and also on the helpful creatures and, because of this, we have a huge problem on our hands.

Ecologists have become a powerful voice now, as they try to make people realize just how important the natural balance of life is, and how the interreactions of all living things are vital to the well-being of the whole system. What exactly do I mean? Perhaps we need to look more closely at energy, this rather difficult concept upon which everything depends.

The greatest energy source we know is our sun, and directly or indirectly this supplies our energy needs. Plants use the energy from sunlight to photosynthesize, or to make sugar from the two available materials, carbon dioxide and water. This sugar is used by the plant as an energy source when it respires, allowing it to grow and flower. Animals are not nearly as efficient as plants and cannot utilize the sun's energy to make food. The herbivores eat some plant source and use the plant's sugar for their food material, and are thus only one step away from the plant source. The carnivores feed on other animals, so the food source will have been transferred at least twice by the time the animal uses it.

Energy is lost each time the food moves from one source to another, so it is fairly easy to see that for a satisfactory existence there must be more plants than herbivores, and that carnivores will be in a minority.

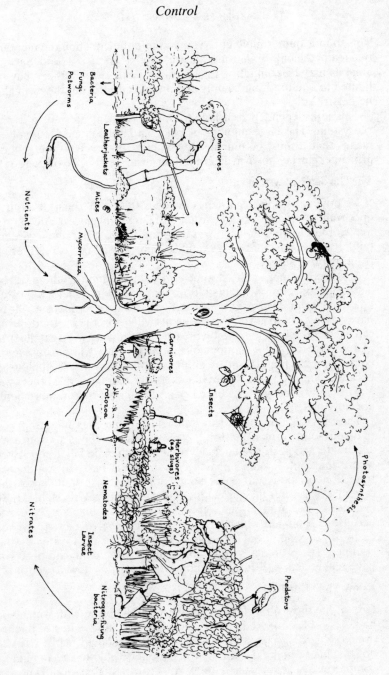

66 The garden ecosystem.

This sounds quite simple until you add into the equation the fact that we are not the only organisms that are 'choosy' about our food. Several animals may be competing for the same items, while others may be limited to one food source only and if that is destroyed, they will also be destroyed.

This interdependence of living things has been referred to as the ecosystem. The large number of plant and animal species involved means that it must be immensely complex, but even so the general principles can be shown in diagrammatic form (see Fig. 66 on page 93).

The Garden Ecosystem

If we now move to the garden, how does this fit in? First of all, it is important to remember that gardens are unnatural places. You may or may not know what the land was used for before it became a garden, but left to its own devices, it would certainly have been very different from its present use.

Most people make at least some effort at gardening, so there will be a strange collection of plants all brought together. Weeds will often be pulled up or destroyed by weedkillers, while other areas might be paved or made into lawns. All the plants will be producing food and all can be a food source for a herbivore (or an omnivore if you eat the fruit and vegetables). This motley collection of plants will encourage an equally mixed population of animals, some of which will flourish because their predators do not like the surroundings, while others will eke out only a meagre existence because not all of their requirements are fully met.

The ones that flourish and are damaging in your eyes may tempt you to try out some form of control. Very few of our methods of control are specific to one pest, so beneficial organisms may be killed too. Even where the control is specific, the death of the pest will result in a reduction of food source for some other organism and upset the system. As a result the garden habitat is not particularly stable, both because of the original plantings and removal of plants by you and because the animals, which may start to reach a balanced state, will be easily upset when you (or your neighbour) decide to attack your enemies. The problem is rather like a maze without an exit: once you have entered, it is difficult to know what to do or how to get out.

Know Your Garden

One of the most important things is to use the brain with which you have been blessed. Remember that you have the greatest influence upon the garden ecosystem, and with a bit of thought, while you will not be able to make it natural, you should be able to reach a happy compromise. The first rule is KNOW YOUR GARDEN. You should know as soon as any plant begins to look sick, if there is a plague of one particular type of insect, or when you are not getting pleasing results from fruit and vegetables. Early diagnosis is always helpful, and often you may exert your controlling influence in the least harmful way. All knowledge gained should be put to use: it may be that it is best to avoid certain plants in your particular area or on your particular soil type, or that an earlier or later sowing may avoid epidemic times. Having made decisions on such matters, you need to go on to observe or find out about two other things: first, you must identify the pest or disease so that you can find out its likes and dislikes; and second, you must do some research to find out which plants are less susceptible to the problems.

PREVENTIVE CONTROL

Most of the descriptions in this book have made some reference to the organism's life cycle – in other words, the descriptions have shown how the organism begins life, what changes it passes through and how it survives the winter. You may think that if an organism lives in our climate, it must appreciate all the seasons, but many organisms will be killed by frost and winter temperatures, so they need some method of survival. If we have a mild winter, many of the organisms which would normally have been killed survive as adults, and these are the years when pests build up to large numbers very early in the season. This observation should immediately produce a warning signal: preventive controls need to be considered where winter weather has been insufficiently cold to reduce the numbers of pests.

It is also important to recognize the pest in its other disguises: for example, larvae are often pests and normally look very different from the adult. Eggs are nearly always tiny and well hidden, and they are rarely easy to identify except when the life cycle occurs rapidly and many generations are found together. Perhaps it is a good thing that eggs are not often discovered, because the question of good or bad can remain unanswered.

You also need to find out about when the organisms spread from one plant to another, both the seasonal time and the factors which affect the spread, such as climate. It may be possible to alter the climate on a local scale – for example, by removing the leaves of the lower part of the plant to allow air movement and reduce humidity – and it may be worth instigating a control method just before migration to new pastures. Natural predators can be extremely useful in preventing the build-up of infection to damaging proportions, but it is necessary to identify the predators and be careful to encourage them, not kill them by other methods of control.

BIOLOGICAL CONTROL

Biology is the study of living things, so biological control of pests and diseases means making use of biological knowledge to control the offenders. The term has been restricted to the introduction of predators, parasites and pathogens (diseases), although there are some more recent concepts, which will be considered at the end of this section. Biological control has been praised by many, most especially because it is a way of avoiding harmful chemicals, and although chemicals have saved many lives, the horror of a few disasters stays long in the memory.

Other advantages, some of which are open to challenge, have been put forward, and there are also some disadvantages (see Table 2).

Table 2

ADVANTAGES	DISADVANTAGES
Control is selective	No 'quick' response
Predator will multiply	Difficult to supervise
No problem of pest developing resistance	Results may vary with external conditions
	Other less important insects may become pests

Throughout this book mention has been made of those animals which are parasitic or predatory and those organisms which can cause disease. The fact that these occur naturally should make us more sensitive and less keen to use non-selective pesticides. Mention was also made of some of the biological control methods which are successfully being used in this country. The research work is slow and confined to the areas of greatest need, which means the gardener's worries will be dealt with only as an aside to work dealing with commercial horticulture and agriculture. Many of our other garden 'aids' have developed as side effects in this way: for example, selective weedkillers came about because hoeing is rather tedious on the field scale, and pelleted seeds were introduced so that the multiseeded sugar beet could be planted as individual seeds, thus avoiding the necessity of thinning.

It is already possible for the amateur to get stock for biological control methods, but it is still easier and cheaper to buy chemicals.

New Ideas for Biological Control

Methods of control which make use of an existing biological system have much in their favour, so many research workers are concentrating their efforts in this direction. Some of the concepts almost verge on science fiction, and it will be interesting to see how many of our problems are overcome in these ways.

Female insects attract male insects by the use of scents referred to as pheromones, which they release from special glands. These chemicals are distinctive to the insect and if they are extracted and synthesized, they can be used to draw the males into a trap. If the male insects are reduced in number, the total population will be reduced to a level at which damage is insignificant. An alternative to a central trap is to have the chemical everywhere, so the males are unable to find the females. This is aptly named the 'confusion' technique!

In Chapters 1 and 6 mention was made of the changes and moults which insects undergo before they become adults. Each stage is controlled by a hormone, and it would be possible to use these hormones as a chemical spray to prevent the insect from growing up.

In Chapter 7 reference was made to the bacteria, fungi and viruses which attack insects, and some of these have already been successfully used to reduce pest numbers. Although such techniques may seem ideal at present, on many other occasions our successes have soon been dampened by an increase in numbers of some other previously insignificant pest.

Pest- and disease-resistant plants are an ideal answer, and while plant-breeders seek for better yields and other attractive features, disease resistance is often top of the list. One way is to make the plant chemically unattractive to pests or diseases; the alternative is to breed physical features which make the plant less susceptible. This might include a very thick, waxy cuticle on the leaf, which would reduce attack by bacteria, fungi and viruses.

We are very used to the idea of inoculation of animals to enable resistance to be developed. This has successfully been done with seedling tomato plants, which can be inoculated with a mild strain of tobacco mosaic virus, as this prevents them from being severely damaged by a more virulent strain.

CULTURAL CONTROL

This is the name given to a logical idea: grow your plants as well as possible and your problems will be minimized. I expect your immediate answer is, 'But I do', and still your garden seems overwhelmed by unwelcome intruders. I will explain which factors need particular attention, and perhaps when you see the reasoning, you will find that there are some areas where your vigilance has not been all it could be.

Land Preparation

The soil can be described as the basic requirement for a garden and it needs to be treated with respect if you want to achieve good results. Many tragedies are blamed upon the soil, but it would often be more realistic to accuse the soil management.

If you want to plant new plants or annual plants such as vegetables, then if possible the land should be completely cleared and dug well before the winter frosts. This will remove both the weeds that can provide homes for pests to overwinter on and also those that can be a source of virus infection. The digging will bring insect eggs and larvae nearer to the surface, and this can be a way of killing them once they are exposed to frost or as they dry out in the winter sunshine. Your friendly robin and other predators will also appreciate your efforts. Some pests will be buried so deep that they can never escape through the depth of soil piled up on top of them. It is as well to remember that predators will suffer in the same way.

The clods of soil will break down during the frosty weather, so when you dig the soil in spring you will find it crumbles. This will encourage your plants to grow well, which is a good start to any healthy garden. Addition of organic matter in the form of well-rotted compost or manure will also encourage strong, healthy growth, and replace many of the nutrients which would have been returned to the soil if the plants had died *in situ*, rather than making a brief appearance on the dining table!

Some nutrients, especially nitrogen, encourage leafy, sappy growth, which many of the sucking pests enjoy, and better results are achieved when a fertilizer high in potassium is used. Soil pH is important for healthy growth too, and it was pointed out in Chapter 7 that fungi are the micro-organisms which predominate in an acid soil. The fungus which causes club root to the cabbage family is worse when the soil has insufficient lime, and liming the soil can often be a successful control method. Waterlogged or badly drained soils are also more prone to problems than well-drained, aerated soils. Cultivations and addition of organic material and a healthy crop of plants will all help to improve drainage and aeration. On the garden scale it is possible to add sand to areas where clay is very bad; once improvement is started, it will usually continue on its own.

Tidiness

Many of our pests and diseases need moist, sheltered conditions for some stages of their life cycles, so they appreciate the gardener who leaves around heaps of garden rubbish, old pots, etc. The problem is not that simple, though, because if the garden is too tidy, the insects that might have eaten the leaves which were already dying may need to attack healthy plants! But if the number of suitable hiding places is reduced, pest numbers will fall too.

Hygiene

Hygiene is important at all times, but care at the early stages may prevent a problem later on. Seed boxes and flower pots should be scrubbed clean or soaked in a sterilizing solution, especially if any infection has been present. Seeds should be sown in healthy soil or compost. Cuttings should be taken only from healthy material; otherwise this can be a very quick way of multiplying your problems.

Sowing and Planting Dates

Some problems can be lessened by careful adjustment of sowing and planting dates. Early sowing may enable the plant to become well established by the time the pest attacks it, so it is well able to cope. Late sowings may miss the main outbreaks of the pest or disease, and often during the warm summer months the plants will easily catch up with earlier sowings. Sometimes it is worth destroying plants earlier than usual to prevent a build-up of pests to spread to other areas.

Species Choice

Certain seeds and plants will be more expensive because the plants are resistant to some of the many problems we have discussed. If your garden has suffered before, then it is certainly worth paying slightly more for resistant strains. Remember that many of the seeds are produced as the result of an artificial breeding programme, so if you decide to keep some seeds for next year, they are unlikely to possess the beneficial properties. Virus-free plants for soft fruits are especially rewarding, so resist the temptation to have plants from a friend.

Crop Rotation

The idea of rotating crops came initially from agriculture and you may feel it has no bearing upon you in your garden. However, there are lessons to be learned from crop rotation. The most important place for it is in the vegetable garden, where crops are best planted in different areas of the vegetable patch in succeeding years. This will help the soil as different species have different nutrient requirements, and also their differing root structures will keep the soil in a better condition. More importantly, any soil-borne pests or diseases would be more prevalent if the same crop followed year after year in the same place.

Companion Planting

If we look at the natural environment we find a complete range of plants growing happily together. Rarely are any plants overpowered by pests or diseases, as some will deter the pests and diseases of others. So, in our gardens it is worth taking care to plan the planting scheme. For example, chives, a member of the onion family, is a herb which can be used as an attractive addition to ornamental beds, where they reduce attacks by pests and diseases. After flowering, cut it and place the material between crops, where it will rot and act as a fungicide. The African marigold, *Tagetes patula*, is a pungent plant and is effective as a deterrent to eelworms and aphids. Spring onions planted close to carrots will reduce attacks by the carrot fly. Some plants do not grow well close to others: for example, parsley with lettuce, potatoes with onions or beans with onions.

This whole topic is one of increasing interest to commercial growers, as well as to the gardener, and hopefully much new useful information will be released over the next few years.

PHYSICAL CONTROL

Sometimes it is possible to afford a certain measure of pest and disease control by physical means. Perhaps the simplest method is hand-picking, when the gardener removes the damaged material and destroys it before it can spread. This can be very important, but obviously it is most effective when an early diagnosis is made. Traps can be very successful on the garden scale: for example, rolls of sacking can provide daytime hideouts for weevils and slugs. Grease bands around trees prevent wingless moths such as winter moth and March moth from climbing up trees to lay their eggs. Slug 'pubs' are another type of trap: a vessel containing beer is slightly buried, the slugs are attracted, fall in and drown!

CHEMICAL CONTROL

Chemical control of pests, diseases and weeds is an emotive subject and we have probably all been involved in lively discussions about pesticides. As with most subjects, a little knowledge can be confusing and the press are quick to dramatize rumours, many of which may later be disproved. We also have to learn from history. It is easy to find traces of DDT in wild animals far from the original source, but on the other hand, this same chemical has saved many people's lives. Different nations have completely different rules about such chemicals, and references in this book conform to UK law. Readers should remember that chemicals banned here long ago may be used on food materials which are imported, and that once chemicals enter the global eco-system, they may ultimately have an influence on our more parochial environment.

The earlier part of this chapter has concentrated on alternatives to chemicals, and many gardeners will be happy to accept some plant damage in the knowledge that their gardens are a haven for a wider range of organisms and that the competition between species will often afford a natural control. On some occasions, however, when damage to plants has been devastating, the gardener may contemplate the range of chemicals available.

In 1985 the Government introduced the Food and Environment Protection Act, followed in 1986 by the Control of Pesticide Regula-tions. This legislation was intended to tighten the safety precautions and ensure the safety of all those coming into contact with pesticides in any way. One of the first actions in late 1986 was the production of a complete register of chemicals which were acceptable as safe and efficient. Many chemicals widely available before that time did not pass the more stringent tests, and so they became illegal. Some of you may have been unable to find a chemical referred to in an older book, or you may have illegal chemicals in your shed. If you are unsure about any product, it would be safest to check in the current edition of the Ministry of Agriculture, Fisheries and Food's pesticides book.

Safety is one aspect which affects us all, but unfortunately the biggest safety hazard comes from the user. Every pesticide label has to be approved and the instructions should be followed exactly. For example, it is safe to use the chemical only on the plants specified, in the way described and at the dose level stated. Hopefully no one would expect to recover from an illness more effectively by taking the whole prescription of pills in one go! In the same way, dilution rates of pesticides are carefully calculated so that the chemical will do the job required and not harm the user or the environment.

Selective use of carefully chosen chemicals may be sensible if one particular problem has got out of hand. The main reason for this may well be that you wish to grow many of one particular plant species and it is impossible for your garden to support the number of natural predators required. Some of the most common problems which gardeners come to me with are about aphids, slugs and snails, two-spotted spider mites, whiteflies, cabbage caterpillars, soil pests like vine weevil, mildew and honey fungus on trees and shrubs. If you refer back to the more detailed information given about these in the text, and also go to Chapter 9, you will see that they are not totally harmful and there may be natural methods for balancing out numbers. If these are insufficient, there are chemical methods which have minimal detrimental effects on the garden ecosystem. I will use the common examples mentioned above to demonstrate the point.

Aphids

If the natural predators like ladybirds and lacewings are unable to keep a colony in balance, it is possible to introduce the fungus disease *Verticillium lecanii* (in spray form) to devastate the population. Alternatively, the chemical pirimicarb is very selective and will kill only the aphids, leaving the predators unaffected to continue their useful work elsewhere in the garden.

Slugs and Snails

Hedgehogs and toads may be absent from your garden, leaving slugs and snails happily devouring vegetation. Aluminium sulphate is a safe chemical for mollusc control, but alternatively metaldehyde tape is much the safest way of applying an effective molluscicide, which is an extremely dangerous chemical in the more usual form.

Two-Spotted Spider Mites

These mite pests in the glasshouse can be well controlled by the introduction of *Phytoseiulus persimilis* (see page 43), but if control is not quite effective, spot spraying the top of the plant with Derris should enable the ideal balance to be reached, and continued control can be left to the predator.

Whiteflies

Whiteflies can be kept under control with the predator *Encarsia formosa* (see page 70), but again, if there is a slight imbalance, a very non-persistent chemical like bioresmethrin can be used to destroy the excess adults.

Cabbage Caterpillars

These pests need to be attacked while they are small and before they have burrowed into the cabbage for food and protection. If you have observed the butterflies in your garden, you can be sure they have laid some eggs which will soon hatch. You may choose to use the bacterial preparation of *Bacillus thuringiensis*, which will slowly kill the caterpillars and then spread to any newly emerged relatives, but a contact, non-persistent chemical such as Derris or bioresmethrin can be used to prevent the small caterpillars growing into destructive pests.

Soil Pests

Pests beneath the ground are always more difficult to control and a chemical will have to be more persistent because the pest may not come into contact with it for some time. However, if the problem is serious enough to warrant chemical treatment, some pests are bound to come into contact with the chemical, so Bromophos would seem to be the least harmful one to use.

Mildews

Mildews affect many different plants but are rarely so debilitating that chemicals are required. However, if control is needed, inorganic sulphur will do the job safely. Care should be taken when sulphur is applied to edible crops.

Honey Fungus and Vine Weevils

These two totally unrelated problems are similar in that there is no effective legal cure once they are established. In both cases you really are dependent upon vigilance and wit to overcome potentially disastrous problems.

INTEGRATED CONTROL

These last few paragraphs have really been an example of integrated control, which is a term that could also be described as 'applied common sense'. In other words, pest and disease control requires thought rather than immediate spraying with the nearest chemical to hand. The pest must be identified, then discouraged by as many means as possible; its enemies must be·encouraged; and only as a last resort should you turn to the use of a specially chosen chemical. Repeated use of chemicals should be avoided as resistance may develop and natural methods will cease to be effective.

On pages 121–3 you will find a list of chemicals which you may consider using. This highlights any notable hazards. If you employ someone to assist you in your garden, they may be qualified to use some other chemicals not available to the amateur. These chemicals are not necessarily more dangerous to the environment but their use requires greater scientific knowledge and skill.

Enjoy your garden and getting to know its residents. They will be pleased to assist you in your work so long as you provide them with their basic needs.

Happy gardening!

9

TOTAL ACTIVITY

This book shows how the different organisms found in a garden interrelate as part of the whole ecosystem. Many of those organisms normally described as pests have revealed a beneficial side, and natural methods for control of pest numbers have been stressed. This final chapter summarizes both the advantages, or beneficial properties of organisms, and those aspects which are distinctly disadvantageous. A closer look will reveal the nature of their activities and show that the majority have at least some beneficial actions.

I hope the following pages will be well thumbed as you become more familiar with both the residents of and the visitors to your garden.

ORGANISM	DISADVANTAGES	ADVANTAGES
Algae pp 77–8	May be unsightly on paths or damp sides of trees	Help soil fertility
Ant p 71	Sometimes loosens plant root systems	Adults and larvae aerate the soil; larvae feed on other soil organisms
Aphid pp 12–13, 44–5	Sucks out plant sap; encourages fungi; may transmit virus diseases	
Bacteria pp 78, 82	Some cause diseases, such as fireblight and leaf spots	Break down organic matter to beneficial humus; soil bacteria make nutrients more available

Total Activity

ORGANISM	DISADVANTAGES	ADVANTAGES
Badger p 20	Produces subterranean burrows; may eat fruit and nuts	Feeds on slugs, snails, insects and rabbits
Bark Beetle pp 62–3	Tunnels in vascular tissue of plants; may carry fungal infections to plants	
Blackbird pp 24–5		Eats worms and insects
Braconids p 69		Parasitize caterpillars, aphids and flies
Bullfinch p 26	Pecks out buds and soft fruit	
Bumble Bee p 67		Pollinates flowers
Bush Cricket p 76		Feeds on aphids and small insects
Butterfly pp 14, 50–4	Larvae feed on plant material	Adults pollinate flowers
Capsid Bug pp 49–50	A couple of species damage fruit trees	Most bugs feed on soft insects and insect larvae

ORGANISM	DISADVANTAGES	ADVANTAGES
Cat p 19	Uses soft soil for toilet activities	Scares off rodents and birds
Centipede pp 10, 11, 34		Feeds on protozoa, mites, insects, slugs and worms
Chafer Beetle pp 16, 64–5	Adults attack aerial parts of plant; larvae feed on roots	
Chaffinch p 27	Pecks at flower buds	
Chalcid Wasp pp 69–70		Parasitizes insect larvae including whitefly
Click Beetle p 64	Larvae (wireworms) feed on roots	
Crane Fly pp 15, 56–7	Larvae (leatherjackets) feed on roots	
Cutworm p 54	Moth larvae feed on roots	
Cynipid Wasp pp 70–1	Produces galls, though these are rarely harmful	

ORGANISM	DISADVANTAGES	ADVANTAGES
Digger Wasp p 68		Feeds on aphids and other insects
Dog p 19	May cause scorch with urine	Chases off cats and rodents
Dragonfly pp 74–5		Predacious on other insects
Earthworm pp 29–31		Aerates the soil; mixes organic matter with soil
Earwig pp 75–6	Distorts dahlia and chrysanthemum flowers	Feeds on aphids

Eelworm *see* NEMATODE pp 10, 31–3

ORGANISM	DISADVANTAGES	ADVANTAGES
Fly Leaf Miner p 55	Larvae burrow through leaf tissue, leaving a scar	
Fox p 20	Their earthworks may cause damage	Feeds on insects, birds and rodents
Frog pp 23–4		Feeds on slugs, worms and insects
Froghopper p 46	Produces cuckoo spit	

GARDEN PESTS AND PREDATORS

ORGANISM	DISADVANTAGES	ADVANTAGES
Fruit Fly pp 58–9		Feeds on rotting fruit
Fungi pp 83–7	May cause diseases such as mildews or rusts	Break down organic matter, especially when woody tissue is present
Fungus Fly pp 58–9	Larvae feed on the young roots of seedlings and cuttings	Feeds on fungus, organic matter and soft insects
Gall Midge p 59	Larvae produce galls on leaf tissue	
Ground Beetle pp 61–2		Feeds on insect eggs, eelworms and soft larvae
Harvestmen p 40		Feed on organic matter, fungi and insects
Hedgehog p 22	Eats berries	Eats slugs, worms, mice and frogs
Heron p 28	Steals goldfish from ponds	
Honey Bee pp 17, 66–7		Pollinates flowers; provides honey

ORGANISM	DISADVANTAGES	ADVANTAGES
Hover Fly pp 57–8		Predatory on aphids
Ichneumon Fly pp 68–9		Parasitizes the caterpillars of butterflies and moths
Lacewing pp 73–4		Larvae are predacious on soft-bodied insects such as aphids
Ladybird pp 60–1		Feeds on aphids
Leaf-cutter Bee p 66	Cuts out areas of leaf for nest construction	Aids pollination
Leafhopper p 46	Sucks out plant sap; encourages fungi; may transmit virus diseases	
Mealy Bug pp 47–8	(as leafhopper)	
Mice p 21	Eat seeds	Eat insect larvae
Millepede pp 10, 11, 33–4	Feeds on roots, seedlings and germinating seeds	Breaks down organic matter

GARDEN PESTS AND PREDATORS

ORGANISM	DISADVANTAGES	ADVANTAGES
Mite *see* SPIDER MITE pp 41–3		
Mole p 20	Produces mole hills	Feeds on slugs, snails, earthworms, millepedes and insects
Moth pp 50–4	Larvae feed on plant material	Pollinates flowers
Mycorrhiza pp 87–8		Help plants absorb nutrients from the soil
Nematode pp 10, 31–3	Some damage plant tissue and may also carry virus infection	Feeds on other nematodes, algae, protozoa, bacteria and organic matter
Pigeon p 27	Feeds on seeds and seedlings	
Potworm p 31		Breaks down organic matter; feeds on fungi, bacteria and nematodes
Protozoa p 82		Help balance the soil micro-organisms
Psyllid pp 46–7	Sucks plant sap; often produces galls	

	ORGANISM	DISADVANTAGES	ADVANTAGES
	Rabbit p 20	Grazes soft green shoots; burrows may be unsightly	
	Robin p 26		Feeds on insects and worms
	Root Fly pp 55–6	Larvae burrow into root tissue	
	Rove Beetle p 62		Feeds on insects, mites and organic matter
	Sawfly pp 71–2	Females 'saw' plant material prior to laying eggs; larvae feed on plant material	
	Scale Insect p 47	Sucks out plant sap	
	Seagull p 26		Feeds on insects
	Slug pp 11, 37–8	Grazes seedlings and leafy material	Helps break down organic matter
	Snail pp 11, 36–7	(as Slug)	(as Slug)

GARDEN PESTS AND PREDATORS

ORGANISM	DISADVANTAGES	ADVANTAGES
Sparrow p 27	Damages brightly coloured spring flowers	Feeds on insects
Spider Mite pp 41–2, 43	Sucks plant material and may transmit virus diseases	Some mites are predatory on other mites
Squirrel p 21	Feeds on nuts, bulbs and fruit	Feeds on insects
Starling p 25	Feeds on berries	Feeds on insects
Symphylid pp 11, 35	Feeds on soft roots and root hairs	
Tachinid Fly p 58		Parasitizes earthworms, snails, beetles, caterpillars and grasshoppers
Thrip pp 48–9	May transmit virus diseases; produces silvering on leaves	Some are predatory on spider mites
Thrush p 25		Feeds on snails and insects
Tit p 26		Feeds on insects

	ORGANISM	DISADVANTAGES	ADVANTAGES
	Toad pp 22–3		Feeds on snails, worms, woodlice, beetles and caterpillars
	True Wasp pp 67–8	Feeds on damaged fruit	Feeds on insect larvae
	Virus pp 88–91	Reduces vigour of plants, sometimes resulting in death	Insect viruses attack larval stages and easily spread throughout the colony
	Vole p 21	Feeds on bark, bulbs and berries	
	Web Spider pp 12, 39–40		Catches and eats aerial insects
	Weevil pp 63–4	Adults attack aerial parts of plants; larvae feed on roots or seeds	
	Whitefly p 48	Sucks out plant sap; encourages fungi; may transmit virus diseases	
	Wolf Spider p 40		Catches and eats ground-loving insects
	Woodlouse pp 11, 35	Feeds on roots and seedlings when there is nothing else available	Feeds on organic matter

GLOSSARY

Acaricide
These are chemicals for killing mites. Some systemic insecticides are also acaricides: e.g., dimethoate.

Active Ingredient
The chemical which is toxic to the pest or disease: e.g., pyrethrum in Bug Gun!

Aerosol
A method of dispersing a chemical in very tiny droplets.

Alternate Host
A host which has to be lived on at some stage in the life cycle before the occupant returns to the original host.

Anti-cholinesterase Compound
A pesticide (organophosphorus or carbamate) which affects the nervous system of mammals. Some people are extra-sensitive and must be careful to avoid contact with these chemicals.

Carbamate
These are man-made chemicals containing carbon, hydrogen, oxygen and nitrogen. They include a wide range of pesticides with an equally wide range of properties.

Concentrate
The pesticide preparation before dilution.

Contact Poison
This kills the pest by coming into contact with its body.

Dust
The chemical comes in a fine powder form: e.g., Derris.

Ecosystem
The community of organisms and their interrelationships.

Fumigant
The chemical is poisonous in the gas or vapour form. Such chemicals are useful for penetrating the soil or using in a greenhouse: e.g., dichlorvos.

Fungicide
This chemical prevents the growth of fungi: e.g., sulphur.

Gall
This is an abnormal growth in or on any part of the plant, caused by some irritation such as a bacterial infection, a pest feeding or the development of a parasitic larva.

Harmful

The chemical is safe if used following the instructions but can be dangerous if used wrongly.

Herbicide
A chemical for killing plants, usually for weed control: e.g., glyphosate.

Honeydew
The sticky, sugary excretion produced by aphids.

Host
The organism which is the home for the pest or disease.

Immune
An organism which will not be infected by the disease.

Inorganic
Technically, these are chemicals which do not contain carbon, but the term is sometimes used to refer to non-natural products.

Insecticide
A chemical for killing insects.

Irritant

A chemical which may produce symptoms such as a rash, watering eyes or sneezing.

Larva
The young form of an insect which feeds actively: e.g., caterpillar.

Latent Infection
The disease is present but shows no symptoms: e.g., cucumber mosaic virus on many weeds.

LD 50 (lethal dose 50)
This figure is often quoted for a pesticide. It is the amount of chemical required to kill 50 per cent of the test species (usually rats, mice or rabbits). A low LD 50 means the chemical is very poisonous to mammals: e.g., Rotenone (50). A high value, more than 10,000 for glyphosate, means the chemical is not very poisonous.

Life Cycle
The changes through which the organism passes until reaching maturity.

Mode of Action (of a pesticide)
The way the chemical kills the pest.

Molluscicide
A chemical for killing slugs and snails: e.g., metaldehyde.

Natural Pesticide
A chemical extracted from natural products: e.g., pyrethrum from the plant *Pyrethrum cinareafolium*. These chemicals are often referred to as organic.

Necrosis
This means the death of part of the plant.

Nematicide
A chemical for killing eelworms.

Nymph
A young insect which is a smaller version of the adult, unable to reproduce: e.g., leafhopper nymph.

Organic Chemical
These are chemicals containing carbon and hydrogen (any other constituents may vary). Organic gardening has altered the definition to mean gardening without the use of man-made chemicals.

Organism
This is a living thing, whether plant or animal.

Organochlorine Pesticide
These are man-made organic chemicals which contain chlorine. DDT is an organochlorine chemical, although it is no longer legal in this country. The commonest example is HCH (Lindane), the main advantage of which is that it is persistent, controlling insects for a considerable time. However, some insects have built up resistance to it. HCH degrades to a less toxic material.

Organophosphorus Pesticide
These are organic chemicals which contain phosphorus. They are very toxic to insects and of variable toxicity to humans, but they are fairly quickly degraded to harmless products. They act upon the insect's nervous system, but as different chemicals work in different ways, it is possible to kill pests selectively. Some pesticides are more persistent than others, so great care should be taken to follow the instructions, especially if you are going to eat the plants you have treated. Many of these chemicals are systemic: e.g., dimethoate.

Ovicide
These are materials for killing eggs, but it has been pointed out that eggs are often well hidden and difficult to reach. The chemicals may be somewhat phytotoxic, as they have to be strong enough to penetrate the egg shell.

Oxidizing

These chemicals will often set themselves alight when in contact with air: e.g., sodium chlorate.

Oxidizing

Parasite
This is an organism which obtains its food by living in or on another organism: e.g., powdery mildew.

Pathogen
This is an organism which causes disease.

Persistent Pesticide
This is a chemical which breaks down slowly so it will continue to be active for some days. Such chemicals are not usually recommended as they are more likely to interfere with the ecosystem.

Pesticide
Any chemical used to kill or control pests, diseases or plants.

Phytotoxic
The chemical is damaging to plant material.

Predator
This is an animal which preys on another: e.g., ladybirds prey on aphids.

Proprietary Name
This is the name by which an individual chemical company markets a pesticide: e.g., ICI's Bug Gun!

Resistant
A pest or disease is resistant to a pesticide if it is no longer killed by it: e.g., some strains of *Botrytis cinerea* with Benomyl.

Rogue
Removal of damaged specimens to prevent the problems spreading.

Saprophyte
This is an organism which feeds on dead material.

Soil Sterilant
This is a chemical for killing pests and diseases within the soil (often as a fumigant).

Spot Treatment
Individual badly infected plants are treated, leaving the majority untreated.

Stomach Poison
The pest has to feed on the pesticide before it is killed.

Synergism
This is when two pesticides mixed together work more effectively than using both chemicals individually. It is illegal to mix your own chemicals, but some proprietary mixtures make use of this effect.

Systemic
The chemical is absorbed by the plants and translocated by the plant vascular system: e.g., dimethoate.

Tolerant
Some plant species may be tolerant of an infection without showing severe disease.

Toxic

The chemical is dangerous. Such products should be used only by a professional who has been trained to use them safely.

Toxic

Translaminar
The pesticide passes across the leaf surface: e.g., pirimicarb.

Trap Crop
This is a plant or plants grown to attract the pest away from other plants.

Vector
An organism which carries a disease from one plant to another: e.g., aphids with cucumber mosaic virus.

Volatile
A chemical which easily evaporates into vapour.

Wetting Agent
A chemical added to a pesticide to improve its contact with plant material.

SOME COMMON GARDEN PESTICIDES

Some Common Garden Pesticides

PESTICIDE Active ingredient	TYPE	ACTION	USE	OTHER DETAILS	LD 50
ALUMINIUM SULPHATE	Inorganic molluscicide	Contact	Slugs and snails	Avoid contact with plant material; causes shrinkage of the pest's slime gland	
BENOMYL	Synthetic fungicide	Protectant and eradicant	Broad spectrum	Interferes with fungal cell division; some resistance problems	more than 10,000
BIORESMETHRIN	Synthetic pyrethroid insecticide	Contact	Aphids, caterpillars	Low mammalian toxicity, but potent to insects	7,070
BORDEAUX MIXTURE	Inorganic fungicide with some bactericidal action	Protectant	Fungal diseases of trees and shrubs	Keep livestock away for three weeks	2,090

BROMOPHOS	Organophosphorus insecticide		Broad range of soil pests	Harvest interval of seven days	720
CAPTAN	Synthetic dicarboximide fungicide	Protectant	Fungal diseases of trees and shrubs	Reduces respiration of fungal spores; banned in several countries	10
DIAZINON	Organophosphorus insecticide	Contact	Insects/mites on ornamentals	Dangerous to bees; harvest interval of fourteen days	300
DIMETHOATE	Organophosphorus insecticide	Contact and systemic	Broad spectrum	Affects insect's nervous system; harvest interval of seven days	180
FENITROTHION	Organophosphorus insecticide	Contact	Broad spectrum	Rapid absorption through skin; dangerous to fish and bees	800
LINDANE	Organochlorine insecticide	Contact, stomach poison and fumigant	Broad spectrum	Dangerous to bees, fish and livestock; follow instructions carefully	40
MALATHION	Organophosphorus insecticide	Contact	Broad spectrum	Dangerous to fish and bees; mammals detoxify	250
METALDEHYDE	Synthetic molluscicide	Stomach poison	Slugs and snails	Dangerous to domestic pets; anaesthetizes pest, which may recover; harvest interval of ten days	600

Some Common Garden Pesticides

PERMETHRIN	Synthetic pyrethroid insecticide	Contact and stomach poison	Broad spectrum	Toxic to bees and fish; rapid knock-down effect to insects	430
PIRIMICARB	Carbamate	Contact, fumigant and translaminar	Selective for aphid control	Restrict livestock for seven days	100
PIRIMIPHOS-METHYL	Organophosphorus insecticide	Contact, fumigant and translaminar	Broad spectrum	Harvest interval varies with crop and application method	1,000
PYRETHRUM	Natural (from *Pyrethrum cineriaefolium*); may include piperonyl butoxide as a synergist	Contact	Broad spectrum	Easily detoxified by light; some insects have developed resistance	584–900
RESMETHRIN	Synthetic pyrethroid	Contact	Broad spectrum	Toxic to bees; quick break-down; harvest interval of one day	2,500
ROTENONE (DERRIS)	Natural	Contact and stomach poison	Broad spectrum	Dangerous to fish and bees; moderate persistence in soil	50
SULPHUR	Inorganic fungicide with some acaricidal action	Protectant and foliar feed	Broad spectrum	Some plants may be damaged	
TAR OIL		Ovicide	Broad spectrum	Only use on dormant parts of the plant: e.g., trunk	

USEFUL ADDRESSES

British Agrochemicals Association
4 Lincoln Court
Lincoln Road
Peterborough PE1 2RP

British Organic Farmers and The
Organic Growers' Association
86 Colston Street
Bristol BS1 5BB

British Plant Gall Society
Dr C. K. Leach (Hon. Secretary)
David Attenborough Laboratories
Leicester Polytechnic
Leicester LE7 9SU

British Trust for Ornithology
Beech Grove
Tring
Hertfordshire HP23 5NR

Friends of the Earth
377 City Road
London EC1V 1NA

Gardencall
403 Silbury Boulevard
Central Milton Keynes
Buckinghamshire

Henry Doubleday Research
Association
The National Centre for Organic
Gardening
Dept. OG1
Ryton-on-Dunsmore
Coventry CV8 3LG

Institute of Terrestrial Ecology
Natural Environment Research
Council
Monks Wood Experimental Station
Huntingdon PE17 2LR

Koppert (UK) Ltd
Biological Control
PO Box 43
Tunbridge Wells
Kent TN2 5BX

Oecos
130 High Street
Kimpton
Hertfordshire SG4 8QP
(Suppliers of Pagoda pheromone
traps)

Organic Garden Centre
Watling Street
Hockliffe
Near Leighton Buzzard
Bedfordshire LU7 9NP

Royal Society for Nature
Conservation
The Green
Nettleham
Lincoln LN2 2NR

Royal Society for the Protection of
Birds
The Lodge
Sandy
Bedfordshire SG19 2BR

The Soil Association
86 Colston Street
Bristol BS1 5BB

FURTHER READING

Alford, D. V., *A Colour Atlas of Fruit Pests*, Wolfe, 1984
Bevan, D., *Forest Insects*, Forestry Commission Handbook 1, HMSO, 1987
British Agrochemicals Association, *Directory of Garden Chemicals*, published annually
Brooks, A. and A. Halstead, *Garden Pests and Diseases*, Royal Horticultural Society, 1980
Buczacki, S. and K. Harris, *Collins Guide to the Pests, Diseases and Disorders of Garden Plants*, Collins, 1981
CAB International, British Crop Protection Council, *The UK Pesticide Guide*, published annually
Carter, D. J., *Butterflies and Moths in Britain and Europe*, Pan Books, 1982
Carter, D. J. and B. Hargreaves, *A Field Guide to Caterpillars of Butterflies and Moths in Britain and Europe*, Collins, 1986
Chinery, M., *The Natural History of the Garden*, Collins, 1977
— *Collins Guide to the Insects of Britain and Western Europe*, Collins, 1986
Chu, H. F., *The Immature Insects*, W. M. C. Brown Co., 1949
Cloudsley-Thompson, J. L., *How To Begin the Study of Spiders*, Richmond Publishing Co., 1987
Cooper, J. I., *Virus Diseases of Trees and Shrubs*, Institute of Terrestrial Ecology, 1979
Dudley, N., *Garden Pesticides*, Soil Association, 1986
Edwards, P. J. and S. D. Wratten, *Ecology of Insect and Plant Interactions*, Edward Arnold, 1980
Fletcher, J. T., *Diseases of Greenhouse Plants*, Longman, 1984
HMSO (Ministry of Agriculture, Food and Fisheries), *Beneficial Insects and Mites*, Bulletin 20, 1969
— *Pesticides*, reference book 500, published annually
Samways, M. J., *Biological Control of Weeds and Pests*, Edward Arnold, 1981
Sankey, J., *How To Begin the Study of Slugs and Snails*, Richmond Publishing Co., 1987
Stubbs, F. B. (ed.), *Provisional Keys to British Plant Galls*, British Plant Gall Society, 1986

INDEX

Algae 77–8, 104
Ants 17, 58, 71, 104
Aphids 12–13, 44–5, 58, 90, 102, 104
  feeding habits 45
  life cycle 13
  reproduction 44

Bacillus thuringiensis 102
Bacteria 78–82, 104
Badger 9, 20, 105
Bees 17, 65–7
  bumble 67, 105
  honey 66–7, 108
  leaf-cutter 66, 109
  life cycle of 17
Beetles 16, 59–65, 90
  bark 62–3, 105
  click 64, 106
  cockchafer 64–5, 106
  ground 61, 108
  life cycle of 16
  rove 62, 111
Blackbird 9, 24–5, 105
Braconids 69, 105
Bullfinch 9, 26, 105
Butterflies 50–1, 90, 105
  life cycle of 14

Cankers 81–2, 86
  bacterial 81
  fungal 86
Capsid bugs 49–50, 105
  apple 49
  common green 49
Carbon cycle 80
  carbon to nitrogen ratio 80
Cats 19, 106
Caterpillars 50–1, 102
Centipedes 10–11, 34, 106
Chaffinch 9, 27, 106
Chrysanthemum leaf miner 55, 108
Control 92–103

biological 90, 97
chemical 100, 103, 121–3
cultural 97, 100
integrated 103
physical 100
preventive 95
Crickets
  bush 76, 105
  house 76
Cutworms 54, 106

Daddy longlegs *see* Flies, crane
Dogs 9, 19, 107
Dragonflies 74–5, 107

Earthworms 9, 29–31, 107
  regeneration 30
  reproduction of 29
Earwigs 75–6, 107
Ecosystem 92–4
Eelworms 10, 31–3, 107
  cyst 32
  leaf 32
  stem 33

Fireblight 81
Flies 54–9, 90
  crane 56–7, 106
  fruit 58–9, 108
  fungus 58, 108
  hover 57, 109
  ichneumon 68–9, 109
  life cycle of 15
  root 55–6, 111
  tachinid 58, 112
Fly leaf miners 55, 107
Food and Environment Protection Ac
  101
Fox 9, 20, 107
Frog 9, 23–4, 107
Froghoppers 46, 107

Fungi 18, 83–4, 102, 108
  beneficial 83
  harmful 84, 87

Gall
  blackcurrant big bug 42
  crown 82
  mite 42
  oak apple 70
  spangle 70
Gall midges 59, 108

Harvestmen 40, 108
Hedgehog 9, 22, 102, 108
Heron 9, 28, 108
Holly leaf miner 55, 107
Honey fungus 86–7, 103
Honeydew 48, 71, 116

Insects 12–18, 44–76

Lacewings 73–4, 109
  brown 73
  green 73
  powdery 73–4
Ladybirds 60–1, 109
Land preparation 98
Leaf eaters 52
Leaf miners 53
Leaf spots 81, 86
Leaf tiers 52
Leaf webbers 52
Leafhoppers 46, 90, 109
Leatherjackets 56–7

May bugs *see* Beetle, cockchafer
Mealy bugs 47–8, 90, 109
Metamorphosis 13–17, 44
Mice 9, 21, 109
  house 21
  wood 21
Mildew 85, 103
Millepedes 10, 33–4, 109
  flat 34
  pill 34
  snake 34
Mites 12, 39, 41–3, 90, 110
  gall 42–3

predatory 43
  red spider 41–2, 112
  two-spotted spider 41, 43, 102, 112
Mole 9, 20, 110
Moths 50–4, 90, 110
Mycorrhiza 87–8, 110

Nematodes 10, 31–2, 90, 110
  feeding habits of 31
  life cycle of 31
  parasitic 32
Nitrogen cycle 79, 80

Organisms 118
  aerial 7
  large 7
  microscopic 18, 77–91
  soil 7

Peach leaf curl 86
Pesticides, common 101, 102, 121–3
Phytoseiulus persimilis 43, 102
Pigeon 9, 27, 110
Potworms 9–10, 31, 110
Protozoa 82, 110
Psyllids 46–7, 110

Rabbit 9, 20, 111
Rats 21
Robins 26, 111
Robin's pincushion 70–7
Rodents 21
Roundworms 31–2
Rusts 85–6

Sawflies 17, 71–2, 111
  birch 72
  gooseberry 72
  rose 72
  slug 72
Scale insects 47, 111
Seagull 9, 26, 111
Slugs 11, 37–8, 102, 111
  feeding 38
Snails 11, 36–7, 102, 111
  feeding 37
  garden 36
  mating 37

Soil pests 102–3
Solomon's seal 72
Sparrow 9, 27, 112
Spiders 12, 39–40
    web 39–40, 113
    wolf 40, 113
Squirrel 9, 21, 112
Starling 9, 25, 112
Stem borers 53
Sulphur cycle 80
Swift moths 54
Symphyla 11, 35, 112

Thrips 48–9, 90, 112
Thrush 9, 25, 112
Thunder-fly *see* Thrips
Tits 9, 26, 112
Toad 9, 22–3, 102, 113

Vertebrates 9, 19–28

Viruses 88–91, 113
    insect 90–1
    spread of 90
    symptoms 89–90
Voles 21, 113

Wasps 17, 65, 67–71, 90, 113
    chalcid 69, 70, 102, 106
    cynipid 70–1, 106
    digger 68, 107
    true 67–8, 113
Weevils 63–4, 113
    vine 103
Whiteflies 48, 90, 102, 113
    glasshouse 70
Wilting, plant 87
Wireworms 59, 64, 106
Woodlice 11, 35, 113
Worms 9, 29–35